RELAX *and Live*

RELAX
and Live

JOSEPH A. KENNEDY

PRENTICE HALL

NEW YORK

To all my associates in the healing art

Foreword

This book has been written for YOU, if . . .

> you would like to learn the art of living with-
> out strain;
> you would like to meet life without a sense
> of pressure, hurry, and worry;
> you are perpetually "all tired out" and don't
> know why;
> you do not sleep well;
> you have lost your zest for living;
> you feel that you are not getting the best out
> of yourself—physically, mentally, or
> morally;
> you have been told to "relax and take it
> easy," but haven't discovered how, or
> feel that your circumstances won't per-
> mit it.

In short, this book is for you, if you want to get more out of life!

In my work as an athletic coach and physical-training director, I learned early that something was missing in the usual physical-training program. We knew how to develop a man's muscles, and we knew practice and conditioning procedures that enabled a man to acquire skill in certain sports. But I found that the man with the best physique did not always make the best athlete; and the athlete who had developed the most skill in practice sometimes found that his skill deserted him in a pinch.

Every once in a while, a young man came along whose appearance was deceptive. You wouldn't pick him out in advance as being exceptional in any way. But when you saw him in action, you realized that he was a natural athlete.

The term "natural athlete" is a good one. It means that the person who is one has practically perfect co-ordination; his movements flow with almost poetic motion. His body seems to be able to think for itself—it does the right thing at the right time, almost automatically.

This perfection does not lie in the man's use of effort or will power. The ability to function without strain or pressure—to let the body perform its actions naturally— is the secret of the star athlete. But—and this is the important point—it is also the secret of all successful, satisfying living.

I have served in the Medical Department of the Department of Physical Education of the U.S. Naval Academy; I have served as Chief Pharmacist's Mate aboard a carrier, the U.S.S. *Lexington;* I have been head of the Department of Rehabilitation at the Pre-flight School at Athens, Georgia; I have worked with business executives at Bill Brown's Physical Training Farm in Garrison, New York; I have been physical-training instructor at

Boys' Ranch, Copperas Cove, Texas; and I am now Assistant Physical-Training Director of the Y.M.C.A. in Atlanta, Georgia. In all of these jobs, I have taught my principles of relaxation.

When working with flyers, I found that twenty minutes of "passive" relaxation immediately after a hard flight left a man feeling as good as new; training in both "rhythmic" and "passive" relaxation did away with such unpleasant effects as preflight "butterflies in the stomach"; pilots reported that they were better able to perceive hazards and dangers, and to take affirmative action and exercise their judgment without becoming unduly excited or scared; students reported that they were able to adjust themselves better to the environment of military life and to the rehabilitation that followed.

In group classes for business and professional men and women, housewives and students, I have seen these principles work.

I am convinced that relaxation can help anyone, regardless of his job, to "do" better and to feel better. I have never met a person who could not learn the technique of relaxation, and benefit from it.

I am convinced, also, that the essentials of relaxation are so easy and so natural that no long weeks or months of training are necessary in order to experience the sense of relaxation. It is true that relaxation is an art and, like any other art, it has to be practiced if one is to become proficient in it. A certain length of time is required for the habit of relaxed activity to "set" so that you find yourself going about your daily tasks without tensions and with a relaxed attitude.

But you should experience a definite sense of relaxation immediately—the first or second time you have someone read my formula to you.

Some time ago I was scheduled to give a first relaxation lesson to the members of the Atlanta Lions Club. A representative of Metro-Goldwyn-Mayer asked if he could send a newsreel cameraman to take pictures of the members "getting the kinks out of their tails." The presence of klieg lights, the knowledge that their actions were being recorded for all the world to see, and the many other distractions that are present when a motion picture is being made, certainly did not create ideal conditions for relaxing. Yet those Lions did relax—and several of them even went to sleep!

There is no magic in my method. It consists of three simple rules, which, if followed, will allow your body to function naturally. Relaxation is natural to the human body; tension is foreign and unnatural. That is why your body rebels against tension and why you feel ill at ease, fidgety and nervous when you are tense, and feel good when you are relaxed. Your body wants to relax and will do so as soon as you give it a chance to.

If you have tried to relax and have failed, or if you think of yourself as one of those who "just can't" relax, give my "three physiological switches" a chance to do the job for you.

I did not invent relaxation. I doubt if you will find

anything new about relaxation itself in this book. I do think you will gain an understanding of relaxation— what it is, what you do and do not do when you relax— and through this understanding learn to relax more easily.

You will not be asked to do anything at all to *make* yourself relax; not once will you be asked to *try* to relax; so, if you have *tried* and failed, give this method of *not trying* a chance.

My method is simple. Do not let its simplicity fool you; relaxation should be easy; don't try to make it difficult.

Synopsis of Method

My system of relaxation is divided into three phases:

1. The Formula for Passive Relaxation which consists of the three physiological switches which "turn on" relaxation in the body;

2. Education in rhythmic relaxation, which teaches you how to carry relaxation into your everyday activities;

3. An explanation of what relaxation is, how it works, why it is beneficial to learn it. This is necessary so that the student will be able psychologically to accept relaxation whole-heartedly.

In this book, I have tried to give you the formula in detail—using the examples, style and language that I employ in personal instruction; I have tried to show you how to recognize and overcome tension in your muscles, not only in the periods of passive relaxation, but also in your day-to-day activities; how to recognize tension-causing factors in your environment, and how to deal with them. I have tried to give specific advice about things to do and not to do.

Everything that I recommend in this book has been tried and has proven effective in my twenty-six years of teaching the art of relaxation.

J. K.

Acknowledgments

I wish to express my sincere thanks to the following for their help and encouragement, without which this book could not have been written:

Alfred A. Weinstein, M. D., Atlanta, Georgia.

The staff of *LIFE* magazine in Atlanta, Georgia.

The staff of MGM newsreel, Washington, D. C. and New York City.

Mr. Hugh Park, and his "Around Town" column in *The Atlanta Journal*.

Mr. W. H. "Tubby" Walton, Atlanta, Georgia.

Mr. George A. Kassabaum, General Secretary, YMCA, Atlanta, Ga.

Mr. Lloyd F. Sanborn, Physical Director, YMCA, Atlanta, Ga.

Radio Stations WSB, WAGA, WGST, and WAGA-TV.

The many civic clubs and other groups which participated in my Relaxation Clinics, and my lectures on relaxation.

The thousands of people all over the world, who helped test and improve my techniques of relaxation.

Table of Contents

Chapter One

How Relaxation Works

A man's wife, his doctor, and his friends caution him to relax and take it easy. He has read psychosomatic medical reports to the effect that tension, in one form or another, is the cause of more than fifty per cent of all illness. He reads in a popular magazine that tension is the villain behind sexual impotence, stomach ulcers, even a form of sinusitis. An advertisement warns him that he must take it easy if he wants his heart to behave.

On the other hand, he has been cautioned all his life not to relax! His mother, his teachers, and his boss have preached a doctrine of ever greater effort.

The point is that we use the word "relaxation" to mean many different things.

For example, during an intensive rearmament campaign, the President of the U.S.A. said that relaxation was the big enemy of our production effort; at about the same time, a prominent medical doctor made the announcement that tension was the greatest enemy of our society, that it killed off our executives in their prime, reduced our work production, created neuroses, and was a destructive factor in all human relations. He concluded that our society must learn to relax if it is to survive.

Back in 1943, *RN, A Journal for Nurses,* ran an article called "Studies in Fatigue and Efficiency." This article stated that time lost from industry in 1941 would have produced 132,000 big bombers, 240,000 medium bombers, 660,000 fighter planes, 3,600 submarines, and 360 large battleships. The article went on to say that fatigue, resulting from physical and emotional tensions, was responsible for most of these lost man-hours and loss in production.

Obviously, we are using the word "relaxation" to mean different things when one authority says relaxation is the greatest enemy of our production effort, and another says that lack of relaxation robbed us of 660,000 fighter planes in a single year!

"Relaxation," as the word is used in this book, means the use of our human machines to promote maximum efficiency and maximum skill. It is a way of functioning; it is a technique for gaining greater mental and physical control of our bodies.

Passive and Rhythmic Relaxation

In this book, I use the term "passive relaxation" to mean complete relaxation—cessation from all effort. We cannot be passively relaxed when we are doing something. To be passively relaxed we must be either lying or sitting down. And when we are *completely* passively relaxed, we are asleep.

When I speak of relaxing while you work, or relaxing while you play, I use the term "rhythmic relaxation."

However, if we think of the contracting and relaxing of muscles in terms of needs and purposes, there is really no hard and fast line between passive relaxation and rhythmic relaxation. For example, rhythmic relaxation means the contracting of a particular muscle only when its contraction is *needed* in a situation, and then letting it return to a state of relaxation as soon as the need for contraction has passed. All the muscles not needed in a certain task are kept relaxed, and those that are needed are contracted only to the required degree of tension. If we follow this plan of rhythmic relaxation all the way through, we will see that when no muscles are needed in a situation, and no degree of contraction is necessary, we will let all our muscles relax completely. Rhythmic relaxation then becomes passive relaxation in a situation that requires no muscular contractions.

The amount of energy used by a muscle when it is contracted needfully is considerably less than the amount of energy used to contract the muscle unnecessarily. A typist who tenses her back muscles unnecessarily and accidentally may very well have much more nerve fatigue at the end of the day than a ditch digger who has used his back muscles with purpose.

Force yourself to do something you do not want to

do, or that you resent doing, and your forcing—making efforts—will cause you to become tense. This is why a monotonous task tires us out so much faster than an interesting one, and why a dull book fatigues our eyes so quickly that we can hardly hold them open, while we may read an interesting one all night.

Energy and Skill

Wasted energy, and the fatigue resulting from tension, do more damage than just making us feel tired and worn out. They impair our skill, and make it more difficult for us to maintain our rhythmic relaxation. Your skill in any psycho-motor performance suffers when you are fatigued—the marksman loses his aim; the typist makes many more mistakes; the schoolboy cannot concentrate; the man behind the machine in the factory loses his precision. Tired people have more accidents than workers with a high energy level. The incidence of accidents during working hours in industry follows the same curve as the energy curve of the workers.

The reason for this is that when our energy level becomes low we unconsciously use more effort, or make more mental demands on our muscles. We unconsciously force ourselves. We resort to the behavior characteristic of the early stages of learning—we make generalized rather than specific efforts. Excess effort works against the successful execution of the psycho-motor process, and so we perform less skillfully.

This is not all. When we work in a tense condition, we upset the whole functioning of the human body. Tense, tired workers are apt to suffer digestive upsets, eyestrain, backaches, and sick headaches.

We are in the midst of a vicious cycle. We become tense because we do not work with rhythmic relaxation. Our tension depletes our energies and makes it still more difficult for us to work with rhythmic relaxation, and so we become more tense.

It is easy to see how passive relaxation practiced daily, and sleeping passively relaxed each night, help us to achieve rhythmic relaxation during the day. During passive relaxation we restore our energy to a higher level, and this enables us to be more rhythmically relaxed in our work. This, in turn, leaves us less fatigued and enables us the better to relax passively at the end of the day. Daily practice in the Formula for Passive Relaxation breaks the vicious cycle and sets up a beneficent cycle.

Nor is this the whole story.

The damage that tension does is not limited to the body. Another result is mental confusion. Just as nerves carry messages from the brain to the muscles, nerves also carry messages from the muscles to the mid-brain. There can be no peace of mind as long as the muscles are rioting. When the muscles are confused, contracting senselessly and without purpose, this state of confusion is relayed back to the brain.

When a person becomes very excited, tense, and anxious, even his five sense organs do not work properly.

He has a blank look on his face; he is not fully aware of what is going on around him or within him; in extreme cases of nervous excitement, he may partially lose his sense of identity, and everything seems unreal.

There is an innate joy and deep-down satisfaction that comes from using our physical bodies as they were meant to be used. As a Physical Director, I have always tried to show people that the value of gymnastic work and the development of athletic skill are much more than the mere development of muscle and the satisfaction that come with the acquisition of skill in some particular sport. Beyond this, there is a deep-down psychological satisfaction that comes from skilled, directed, and successful functioning of the human machine.

Many tense people I have worked with did not realize, until they began to relax, that their tenseness had robbed them of a portion of their sensory awareness of the world about them. Later, many of them have told me: "The whole world looks different to me, now that I've learned to relax"; or "I get more fun out of just ordinary things"; or "It seems that I have become more alive"; or "I feel that I have really begun to live";— which is what prompted the title of this book.

The "Secret" of Learning How to Relax

After *Life* magazine ran an article on my method of relaxation, I received letters from people all over the world, a great many of them asking, in one form or another: "What is your secret?" When a picture magazine from Holland wrote me for information to use in a story, they said: "Please give us a few words about your secret of relaxation."

The more I thought about it, when answering those letters, the more I realized that there is a "secret," or knack, of learning relaxation, and that the success I had had in teaching people to relax was probably due, in large part, to my ability to impart to them, perhaps somewhat unconsciously, this "secret."

The "secret" is that if you would relax, you must concern yourself with the means and not the end. You get relaxation indirectly.

In my relaxation classes, students are not told to *try* to relax, but are shown just how to go about the simple business of releasing individual muscles and muscle groups. When they concerned themselves with this simple business, many of them reported that they relaxed without realizing it. This is not only the most effective method, but the easiest. Students do not get involved with motives, results, or whys and wherefores. They just follow the simple steps in the formula and find themselves relaxed.

Don't TRY to Relax!

Relaxation is not something you *do;* it is something you *don't* do. Doing requires effort, and effort makes tension. You relax when you stop doing, when you stop making efforts.

So do not *try* to relax. So ingrained is the vicious habit of making efforts, of striving and straining, that many people unconsciously become tense in their efforts to learn to relax!

The physiological condition that is characterized by a subjective feeling of ease and well-being, calm, mental control, and that is accompanied by a dilatation of the blood vessels which gives one a pleasant, warm feeling, or glow; the lack of nervousness, strain, and pressure— these effects of relaxation are not subject to voluntary control, and cannot be obtained by trying.

Yet it is just these effects that the average person thinks of when he thinks of trying to relax. He strives to achieve these end results directly, and he fails, because the end results of relaxation cannot be obtained that way. They can be obtained only by your doing the specific things you are asked to do in the formula. Then relaxation comes as surely as the light in your ceiling comes on when you throw a switch.

The Three Physiological Switches

My formula is a series of three physiological switches. If you concern yourself only with turning on the switches, and do not concern yourself at all with the results, relaxation is sure to come.

Sometimes I find it necessary to tell a student over

and over again: "I am not asking you to do something new, or strange, or difficult. All I am asking you to do at the moment is to let go your jaw muscles—to stop doing what you do when you clench your jaws. Right at the moment we are not concerned with the consequences —although no serious harm can come from dropping your jaw for a moment; we are not concerned with deciding whether you ought to relax, whether this will help you, or with anything else except the loosening up of your jaw muscles. If you know how to clench your jaws together, you know how to unclench them. Remember that this simple thing is all that I am asking you to do."

Although such instruction may seem elementary and somewhat childish to some people, I have found that it works. I have found such instruction particularly beneficial to those persons who say that they have tried for years to relax and have failed.

When people make an effort to obtain the end results of relaxation and fail, relaxation for them ceases to be something simple and manageable; it becomes something magical. There is no mumbo-jumbo about relaxation; there is no magic about it; no luck. It is a natural physiological process that follows physiological laws. Concern yourself with the *causes,* and the *effects* will take care of themselves. If you can perform such a simple task as clenching your fist together tightly, and then stop clenching it and let it go, you can do all that you need to do in order to relax. The formula will show you how to do the same simple thing with your fore-head, jaw, neck, and abdomen, until you have stopped clenching your entire body.

If you are told to wrinkle your brow into a frown, realize that this simple act is all that you are required to do. Let the act be an end in itself. Do not worry about its significance or its effect. Merely wrinkling the brow into a frown is a simple, easy thing that anyone can do. Do it right now, if you aren't doing it already! It is just as simple and easy to let your brow unwrinkle. Do that now. This simple act is something definite and manage-able that is subject to your voluntary control. It is some-thing you *can* do. There is no need to get excited about it, or to feel anxious.

Trying to deal with the mysterious and unknown causes tension. Unless we know exactly how we can take hold of a job and gain some sort of control over it, we always make excess efforts. The three simple steps of my formula for passive relaxation bring relaxation out of the realm of the mysterious into the realm of the known and simple. They are things you can do without strain, without a feeling of difficulty, and without a feeling of personal inadequacy.

People often ask me: "What am I to think about when I am relaxing?" The answer is: "Think about fol-lowing and putting into practice each individual instruc-tion as it is given. Do not try to think; do not try to concentrate. Thinking and concentrating imply effort.

Remember that *relaxing* is the reduction of effort; *relaxation* is the absence of effort."

The Error of Impatience

Most tense people are impatient. They want results directly and immediately, but they do not want to bother with the simple steps that lead to the results. In sports, they are the fellows who want a fine backhand drive in tennis, but never are willing to go through the hours of slow, patient and relaxed practice necessary to develop it. As a consequence, they play a mediocre game all their lives.

Albert Tangora, for many years world's champion typist, used to advise students: "Don't be in a hurry to type fast. Don't worry about speed at all. That will come. Concentrate on accuracy—on striking just one key at a time, taking all the time you need to strike the right one."

Ben Hogan practiced his golf shots over and over—mechanically and with no sense of pressure. It required several years of this steady, relaxed practice for him to bring his swing to its ultimate perfection.

This does not mean that learning to relax must be a long, drawn-out process. Learning to relax is not as difficult as learning a golf swing.

Actually, passive relaxation is not something we must learn. It is something we need to relearn. Every baby knows how to relax passively. Relaxation is natural.

Relaxation is as natural as breathing. I often tell students that it is as easy as breathing and that if you can breathe, you can relax. We have to learn how to contract our muscles properly, but we do not have to learn passive relaxation—it is born in us and is as much a part of us as our breathing. Yet we do need patience, or a relaxed attitude, about learning to relax.

I have known people who spent fifteen years trying to relax. These impatient people spent fifteen years in the attempt and still had never learned to relax. Yet most of them relaxed the *very first time* they used the formula as it should be used—that is, by concerning themselves with the individual instructions, one by one, rather than by making a general effort to try to obtain relaxation.

The Three Steps of the Formula

These are the three physiological switches that turn on relaxation:

1. Recognizing tension and learning to reduce it, partially or completely, by the simple method of stopping what you're doing to cause it
2. Reduction of the breathing cycle
3. Reduction of mental imagery.

Each step will be explained in detail in subsequent chapters. But because I do not want to add to your tension by making you impatient, I am going to give you my formula in the next chapter. Do not try to use it yourself. Read it over first, so you know what it's all about, but don't expect to get much help from the reading. Then try out my method by having someone read the formula to you. Then, in your newly relaxed state, read the rest of the book—to find out why the formula works, and to learn a lot more about yourself and other people.

Chapter Two

The Formula for Passive Relaxation

Relaxation is a sensation. You do not do it; you get the feel of it. The easiest way to get the feel of it is to avoid reading, thinking about, remembering, or trying to apply instructions. That is why it is important that you do not try to use the formula by yourself. Have someone read it to you. As the instructions are read, do not try to think—just obey them as automatically as possible, in much the same way that you come to a stop at a red light, automatically, without bothering to think about it.

Many years ago, in my physical-training work, it came to my attention that a muscle tends to relax by itself if the process of relaxation is begun immediately after a period of tension, and the conscious attention is shifted to other matters. Animals use this method when they stretch and yawn just before going to sleep. Stretching brings the muscles to a peak of contraction, where the relaxation can be *felt* and experienced, as the muscles begin to let go immediately after the stretch. From this peak of contraction the animal is able to start relaxing the muscles. He then leaves them alone and allows them to continue the relaxation that has been begun.

We might call this the principle of inertia as applied to skeletal muscles. If you remember your high school physics, you know that the law of inertia is that a body at rest has a tendency to remain at rest, and a body in motion has a tendency to remain in motion. Translating freely from physics to anatomy, we might say: a muscle that has started relaxing has a tendency to continue to relax, if it is not interfered with by conscious effort.

In the formula we do not attempt to keep the attention upon a muscle until all residual tension has been consciously relaxed away. Instead, we start the process of relaxation, and then immediately shift the attention away to another muscle, allowing the first muscle to continue its relaxation automatically and subconsciously. From the very beginning, the formula encourages subconscious and habitual relaxation.

Also, notice that you do not do anything in order to relax. Your conscious doing, or effort, is directed toward tensing a particular muscle. To relax it, you merely stop this doing, stop making an effort, and let the muscle relax. In using the formula, keep in mind that a particular muscle continues to relax after you have taken your attention away from it, and will relax completely only after you have done so. Therefore, when you are working with a particular muscle, do not examine it anxiously to see if it is relaxed. Just start the relaxation; then leave it alone and forget it.

How to Use the Formula

After you have practiced with a reader * for about a week, try giving yourself instructions to relax. Repeat the instructions to yourself mentally, and follow them. You will find you can relax and obey the instructions without effort, just as if someone were reading them to you. After a still longer period of practice you will find that you can forego the instructions altogether. You will have learned relaxation, and will be able to relax almost instantly, at will. However, do not be too impatient, and expect to reach this stage too soon. We must crawl before we walk, and walk before we run.

I suggest that you devote one hour a day to passive relaxation. No matter how busy you are, I think you can afford to spend an hour relaxing. The time spent in relaxing will, in the end, enable you to get more done. But if you think you have only fifteen minutes to devote to the formula, use that time; even five minutes are better than no time at all.

---

* While it is not essential to have the formula read to you, it is decidedly preferable. Ask someone to read it, if possible; but if that is completely out of the question, to read it yourself is better than missing it entirely. Another course is to write to the Publisher (Dept. RL) for information about the phonograph record which gives the instructions as I give them in my own relaxation classes.

When to Use the Formula

Try using the formula not only during your regular practice periods, but also at other times—when you are emotionally upset, extremely fatigued, when you have a nervous headache—have someone read the formula to you. People with nervous stomachs and finicky appetites can derive benefit from having a friend read the formula to them before dinner. So can the overweight, compulsive eaters who unconsciously use food to allay inner tensions.

One lady told me that she uses the formula for half an hour before any important social engagement, and that she not only feels better and enjoys herself more, but that her friends remark about her new personality, her sparkle and magnetism.

Athletes can use the formula with benefit before an important contest; public speakers can use it to rid their stomachs of butterflies just before a speech; business executives can use it to be more poised, collected, and clearheaded just before an important deal.

Preparation for Relaxation

First, be sure to loosen constricting clothing at the neck, waist, knees (garters), and ankles.

The sitting position: Then, if you are sitting in a straight chair, assume a comfortable posture, both feet flat on the floor, the hands lying easily across the thighs. Hold your head in any way that seems restful to you; drop it toward the chest if that seems best. If you are using a contour-type chair, just "jelly" yourself into the most restful position.

The bed position: You may choose your own position—lie on your back, hands at your sides, with or without the wrists supported by a light padding of any soft material; the back of the knees may also be supported, if you wish. Or, you may choose to lie prone or semi-prone with one leg flexed. In either of these positions you may have a pillow for head support. Do not extend your arms overhead. They will have a tendency to go to sleep, and cause tension in hands and fingers. No part of the body should be supporting another part——don't lie on an arm, or have one leg crossed over the other. You should feel as if you were floating on water with your body buoyed up, and all parts of it completely supported, with no strain.

DO NOT READ BEYOND THIS POINT

Instructions to reader: Just before the session is to begin, direct the student to get ready by asking him to remember things or events that had a pleasant ending. The room should be well ventilated and should be as dark as possible. A small book light attached to your book will make it possible for you to read and have the rest of the room entirely dark. Read the formula matter-of-factly. Do not attempt to put expression into your voice. Just read clearly and distinctly, smoothly, and not too fast. Pause slightly at the end of sentences, or where a pause is indicated by these marks . . .

The Formula

Close your eyes and turn your eyeballs downward as if you were looking at a black spot on the tip of your shoe.

What you are going to be asked to do is easy. There is nothing mysterious or strange about it, nor is it anything that you do not already know how to do. To demonstrate, I want to give you a preliminary briefing on tension.

Slowly close your right fist tightly. That muscular contraction that you feel all the way up to your shoulder is . . . tension. Remember this definition—tension is muscular contraction. Also, remember the feel of it. Now, slowly unclasp your fist and . . . let go. That muscular limpness that you feel is . . . relaxation. Remember this definition—tension is muscular contraction . . . relaxation is muscular limpness. That is all there is to relaxation.

We are now ready for the first step of the formula, which is . . . recognition of tension, and dropping it. We are going to cover the entire body, head to toes, front then back.

Direct your attention to . . . *the forehead*.

Frown—you experience tension in the forehead. Let go—the brow smooths out and the muscles become limp.

Direct your attention to . . . *the eyes*.

You have been told to keep them closed all the time, and rolled downward. Continue to look at that imaginary black spot on your shoes. We will return to the eyes later.

Direct your attention to . . . *the jaw*.

Clench your teeth together—notice the tension in the point of your jaw. Let them go—stop clenching them. Feel the weight of your lower jaw as it sags. Let it continue to sag until the teeth are about a quarter of an inch apart. Let your tongue rest loosely on the floor of your mouth.

Direct your attention to . . . *the neck*.

If you are lying on your back, draw the head forward off the pillow; otherwise, draw your chin toward your chest. Here you have tension in the front neck muscles. Let go—drop the head back to its original position.

Direct your attention to . . . *the shoulders*.

Shrug your shoulders as though you were saying: "I don't know." Here you have tension in the muscles that help support the head, and also tension in the shoulder girdle. Let go—drop the shoulders down with a sigh.

Direct your attention to . . . *the arms*.

Close both fists tightly and stiffen the arms. Here

you have tension in both arms up to the shoulders. Let go—let the fingers spread out and become loose.

Direct your attention to . . . *the chest.*

Breathe in deeply. Here you have tension in the chest wall. Let the air go with a big sigh, as if you were an actor on the stage and wanted to convey to the audience that you have just passed through a crisis, and that now all your troubles are over. As you sigh, let the chest wall collapse.

Direct your attention to . . . *the abdomen,* or *stomach.*

The abdominal region is of great importance because of its many nerve plexuses. The most commonly known of these is the solar plexus. A plexus is a sort of fuse box with a lot of lines leading to it, these lines being nerve trunks that control the adjacent viscera (organs).

Tense the abdomen, or stomach, as it is commonly called. You can feel this contraction if you will pretend that a friend is playfully making a move to deliver a punch in the pit of your stomach. Let go the tension. Imagine that there is an iron plate in front of your stomach that will protect you from all blows. You do not need to defend yourself any more.

Direct your attention to . . . *the thighs.*

If you are sitting, contract the front thigh muscles by pushing slightly downward and outward with the feet against the floor. If you are lying prone, straighten the legs at the knees. Here you have tension between the hips and the knees, or what is commonly known as the lap. Let go. Stop doing what you were doing to cause the tension.

Direct your attention to . . . *the legs and feet.*

Bend your feet at the ankles and bring the toes upward toward the knees without bending the knees. Here you have tension in the calves and feet. Let go—by letting the feet extend downward away from the body, as a dog or cat does for body-stretching and relaxation.

We have now covered the front part of the body, contracting the muscles from head to foot so that you could feel tension, and then feel relaxation. These parts will continue to relax as we direct our attention to the back of the body.

Direct your attention to . . . *the head and neck.*

Draw the head backward. Here you have tension in the back of the head and neck. Let go by dropping the head slowly forward to its original position.

Direct your attention to . . . *the shoulders.*

Draw the shoulders backward as you would if given the command, "Attention," in a military drill. Here you have tension between the shoulder blades and throughout the shoulder girdle. Let go by dropping back to your original position.

Direct your attention to . . . *the back.*

Bend backward at the hips—causing both your shoulders and legs to press down against the bed or chair.

Now, let go by dropping back to the original position. This movement also covers the back of the legs.

Now we come to step two—lowering the breathing cycle.

The breathing cycle of the normal adult ranges from 18 to 20 respirations a minute. One respiration is an inhalation, an exhalation, and a period of rest. We will endeavor to lower this respiratory cycle to from 10 to 14 inhalations and exhalations a minute. If we pay conscious attention to the breath entering and leaving the nostrils, this will lower the breathing cycle automatically and make it smoother. Do not try to force yourself to breathe slowly all at once. But begin now consciously to breathe gently and smoothly. Notice your breath as it enters your nostrils on each inhalation, and as it leaves your nostrils on each exhalation. Let your breathing grow a little slower. In doing so you lower the oxygen intake and this automatically slows down nerve function, and the function of the body in general. We are doing, in effect, the same thing we would do if we were banking a fire for the night during the winter. You bank a fire because you do not need all that heat and do not want the useless expenditure of coal burning during the night. In the same way, the body does not need to take in as much oxygen during the night as it does during an active working day. This slowing down of body function hastens complete relaxation when it is combined with steps one and three. Keep right on paying attention to the stream of breath entering and leaving your nostrils and allow it to become as gentle and smooth as possible.

Now, we have step three—mental imagery.

Do not try to blot out your worries, obligations or duties by force. Instead, just say to yourself: "Training in passive relaxation is important to me. There is nothing else in the world that I ought to be doing at this present moment." Dare to relax. Let yourself relax.

For complete passive relaxation our goal should be the obliteration of all imagery from the mind. However, we do not do this by trying to make the mind a blank, or by trying to think of nothing. Trying to think of nothing is trying to think of a something, and to make it more difficult, a something that is not at all clear in your mind.

For our purpose, we may say that mental imagery is obliterated from the mind when we are visualizing, imagining, or remembering black perfectly. Just as the perfect color black is the absence of all light reflection or objective imagery, when we think black, there is no mental imagery, no effort made to look or see mentally. When you remember black, in effect you turn out the light on mental activity.

So, do that. Turn out your mental light on yesterday, today, and tomorrow. Remember having seen black. To do this you do not make an effort actually to see black with your physical eyes. Just remember having seen some black object in the past. You may remember whatever black object is easiest for you—a black telephone, a black pair of shoes, a black letter seen in a book, black coal, black velvet drapes. Remember how it would look if you were in a completely light-proof room and drew thick black velvet drapes over the windows. Imagine yourself standing before a wall or screen painted the blackest black you can imagine. Remembering a small black period on a page is best of all, but remember whatever black object it is easiest for you to remember, and you can even shift from one black object to another, if you wish.

By following steps one, two, and three you have started your whole body on the road to relaxation. Now just give yourself up and make no more efforts—to follow instructions, or to learn relaxation, or to do anything else. Just let yourself go, and rest quietly without trying to do anything at all. Tell yourself that you are going to rest a bit from your relaxation lesson. The experience of relaxation, like that of sleep, is not something you do. It is something that comes when you stop trying.

I have deliberately made the formula as brief and simple as possible. It is designed for those who cannot devote much time to a relaxation program. Make it a part of your going-to-sleep routine. If you are consistent in your application of the formula, you will achieve a high degree of skill and finesse in getting the desired results—relaxation at the times when you need it most, and sleep at night. I say this with emphasis and sincerity because of the success I have had with large groups, using the formula exactly as it is given here. It is my opinion that since it has worked already for thousands, it will also work for the readers of this book.

Chapter Three

Recognizing Tension—and Dropping It

In her book, *Mind and Body* (Random House, New York), Dr. Flanders Dunbar points out that one of the most widespread illnesses of our civilization is the inability to relax. In her work she has found that most people who suffer from this illness do not even suspect that they have it, until it has been complicated by some other ailment. "Teaching them how to relax is one of the most valuable of the psychosomatic techniques," says Dr. Dunbar.

There is an old saying among baseball players: "You can't hit it, if you can't see it." In my relaxation classes, I paraphrase this by saying: "You can't relax tension, if you can't recognize it."

Most of us simply do not realize the fact that in practically all of our everyday activities we are driving with the brakes on. We have worked and played in a tense condition for so long that we have come to regard it as more or less normal. We have developed a blind spot for tension, somewhat in the same way that a person who works in a chemical plant for any length of time soon becomes unaware of the odors about him, simply because he doesn't pay any attention to them.

Yet, until we have learned to recognize our real enemy and deal with him, it is practically impossible for us to achieve the calm, collected state we desire. When we try to be calm, we make a generalized effort which usually results in making us more tense. It is only when we come to recognize that we must deal with tension, the cause, and not nervousness, the effect, that we begin to have some success. We then direct our attention specifically to dropping the tension that is present in our brows, jaws, arms and other parts, rather than to trying to fight fear, overcome nervousness, or make ourselves calm.

One of the purposes of the formula is to help you to acquire directed intentional contraction of your muscles. It also makes you aware of your unconscious tension, shows you what it is, and so enables you to deal with it by dropping it. This is what we do in step one of the formula. We begin teaching your muscles what tension is. As they learn tension and begin to let it go, your muscles get the experience of relaxation—which is merely the sensation that accompanies the absence of tension.

How We Control Our Muscles

To use our muscles in work or play is to employ a psycho-motor skill. Both mental and physical processes are involved. Making our muscles do what we want them to do is a skill that must be learned. You see a book on the table before you, decide to pick it up, reach to get it, scarcely aware that you are performing a complicated act that required many hours of practice and learning.

Yet, as an infant you had no control over your muscles. Your body was a machine or an instrument that you had to learn to play. The learning processes that you went through are very similar to the learning processes that take place when, as an adult, you learn to play a piano, use a typewriter, or develop a groove for your golf swing. If you watch a baby when he is first beginning to use his arms and legs, you will observe that his hands do not always do what he wants them to do. He soon finds that he cannot control them by sheer will power. If he reaches for a rattle, he is apt to miss it; if he tries to move his hand to the right, he may move it to the left instead. Yet, instinctively, he keeps thrashing about. Finally, by trial and error, his hand does go where he wants it to go. He remembers the feel of the successful attempt and begins to build a link between his mental images and his doing. He then tries to reproduce this success. After more trial and error he is again successful. The tie-in between mental image and doing is strengthened, and after much more practice, he begins to learn the skill of playing his physical instrument—or learning to make his muscles obey his mental images.

Now let us consider the degree of skill that we have in playing our human instrument—controlling and using our muscles skillfully and efficiently.

Everything that you do—walking, talking, washing dishes, signing your name, looking, even thinking—is a psycho-motor skill. Most of us put forth too much effort, and use muscles entirely unnecessary for the task at hand. We contract muscles that are not involved in the act, and even contract opposing muscles.

As a physiotherapist, I have assisted many people in learning to use their limbs again after long disuse (caused, for example, by temporary paralysis, or by a prolonged rest cure in bed) had erased the link in the phycho-motor chain, or after they had lost the tie-in between imagery and doing. In these cases, the physio-therapist uses the same technique that the baby uses. No physiotherapist would be so foolish as to tell one of these patients to use will power, or to move his leg simply by making an effort to do so. Instead, the physiotherapist seeks to rebuild the link between mental image and mus-cular doing. He moves the patient's limbs in the desired direction. The patient concentrates on the sensation, or feel, when the limb goes where it is supposed to.

The psycho-motor mechanism has all the elements of a conditioned response. What takes place within the body when our muscles respond to our images is not very different from what took place in Pavlov's classic experi-ment with dogs. Every day, for several weeks, he sounded a bell a few seconds before placing food before the dogs in his laboratory. Then he found that the mere ringing of the bell was sufficient to cause the dogs to salivate, whether food was brought or not. Pavlov said that his dogs had become conditioned to salivate at the sound of a bell. The bell was the stimulus, and the salivation was the conditioned response.

If we substitute mental image for the bell, and controlled muscular contraction for salivation, we have a picture of what happens in our bodies when we do something with our muscles. One of the characteristics of a conditioned response is that it is automatic. When the stimulus is presented, the response follows as a matter of course. No effort or will power is required.

Muscles obey mental images. When our muscles are working perfectly, they respond to our mental images somewhat automatically, and with a minimum of conscious effort on our part. Most of the time when we feel called upon to use will power, or make some additional effort, what we really need is more faith in our minds and muscles to do their work properly. We should feel that it is our muscles that make the effort, and that they will work for us if we trust them to do their work, instead of trying to coerce them. They work better when we speak our orders quietly than when we shout at them.

In your daily practice in passive relaxation—in recognizing tension and dropping it—you learn to recognize what it is you do or don't do to relax muscles. This is also what you do or don't do to relax effort.

I have found that this physiological approach is the best one. Try to control your thoughts or put worry out of your mind, and you are apt to find it all but impossible. But you *can* learn to control your muscles. You will find that the best way to control your thoughts and emotions is to do whatever it is you do when you relax your muscles.

You have to do something to feel afraid, to worry, to be nervous, to be anxious, to be mentally upset, and to be emotional. In short, you must make an effort. Any time you make an effort, muscles contract. Relax your muscles and you are not making an effort. When you are not making an effort, it is impossible to worry or be impatient or anxious. There is an old Hindu saying: "He who cannot control his muscles cannot control his mind."

What Is Tension?

"Effort," as I use the word in this book, is the mental demand made upon muscles to act—the orders that are issued by the "conscious I." Excess effort results in unnecessary or excess contraction; what we commonly speak of as tension. It is inherent in the very nature of learning that conscious effort tends to decrease as proficiency and skill increase. The new piano student must painstakingly think out each move he wants his fingers to make. He does not become an accomplished pianist until he can play somewhat automatically—without thinking—until he almost lets the piano play itself. In the same way, the human body performs when we let it go, rather than drive it.

While we are learning a skill it is necessary for us to practice certain actions consciously. *When we have learned* the skill these conscious efforts are not only unnecessary but become an impediment. Let the pianist or the typist begin to think about his fingers and he is likely to make a mistake. Let the dancer try to manipulate his feet consciously, and he loses his timing and stumbles. Make an effort to speak correctly and you stutter or become tongue-tied. When the vocal muscles become tense from effort they simply cannot perform as they should.

Much the same thing happens when you stare at an object. In order to see perfectly, the eyes must make numerous minute movements—scanning the object under observation. This scanning is as automatic as a reflex; it is no more subject to your will than is your heart beat. When you stare—make a conscious effort to try to see—the eyes become tense. They do not scan as they should. Sight suffers. If you stare hard enough—and make your eyes absolutely immobile—you cannot see at all after a few seconds.

Stuttering and staring are only two examples of the way effort and tension upset psycho-motor processes. Not so obvious is the fact that many tense people "stare" all over. They stare in their thinking, their walking, in batting a ball, or in signing their names.

Why is it that a man who is poised and self-possessed, and whose ideas reel themselves out effortlessly in his own study, suddenly finds his mind a blank when he is attending an important board meeting? Why is it that you cannot think of a thing to say in answer to an insulting or a clever remark at a party, but on the way home, when you aren't trying, the perfect reply pops into your mind without any effort at all? In all these cases we have become tense from making an excess effort. We have frozen up and jammed the psycho-motor mechanisms.

In sports, we call this pressing. The batter who presses to make a hit interferes with his unconscious groove and misses the ball. We have all had the experience of trying hard to remember a name or address, only to have it elude us the more, until finally we gave up our conscious efforts and it popped into our minds. We relaxed and let our minds work for us. The same thing happens when a radio or TV quiz contestant freezes up and misses the answer to a question that would be easy for him if he were sitting relaxed in his own living room.

Most people recognize that tenseness interferes with the execution of a skill once it has been learned. But it is equally true that tension interferes with the learning itself. If learning is to be complete and effective, the first stage—when we consciously practice directing our muscles—must be done in a relaxed manner. Forcing, pressing, hurrying, or practicing under pressure, keeps the subconscious from learning the skill as it should. If we practice in a tense, anxious state of mind and body, we keep our subconscious from really learning the skill as it should. We continue to perform with a certain amount of conscious direction and effort. Everyone has noticed the ease of the really accomplished performer, the effortless way in which he goes about his business. Excess tension in the human body is an indicator of unskilled performance, lack of proper mental control, and waste of energy, just as striking the wrong notes on a piano keyboard is an indication of ineptness.

Recognizing Tension

At this moment, your body is receiving many impressions which you may not be consciously aware of. There is the weight of this book in your hands, the pressure of the back of the chair against your back, the touch of the clothes upon your body. A clock may be ticking. And, unless you have been trained in relaxation, I can almost guarantee that there is a sensation of tenseness in your muscles.

How can you become conscious of this unconscious tension? First, by making the tension consciously directed; second, by paying attention to the sensation you experience as you do so. Unconscious tension is muscular contraction that you do without meaning to, without conscious will, and without knowing what you are doing. The important thing is that you *can* produce tension consciously.

Let's repeat, for emphasis, a simple experiment that we tried earlier. Up to this point, have you been aware of any tension in your forehead? Probably not, but there's a good chance that it is tense. In order to recognize the unconscious tension in your forehead, let's *deliberately* and *consciously* produce more tension there.

Wrinkle your forehead into a frown, and consciously pay attention to the *feeling* in the forehead muscles as you frown. Now the tension in your forehead is not unconscious, but conscious. You now have some idea of what this tension is—how it feels. Tomorrow, after you've been working at your job for several hours, stop for a moment and ask yourself, "Am I aware of any tension in my forehead?" and you will probably be able to detect the faint sensation of tension already present there.

As you use the formula and practice paying attention to the sensation of tension you produce consciously just before letting the muscles go, you will find that your perception of tension becomes more and more acute. At first, you will detect what you think is all the tension present in a muscle, and you will be able to untense it. But as you practice, you will find a degree of tension present that you were not aware of before. This can also be dropped, once it is recognized. One student told me: "When I started learning to relax, I discovered layer after layer of tension of which I had been wholly unaware before my daily practice with the formula began."

This recognition of tension comes not from mental theorizing, but from practice—practice in using the formula. You may say that you don't need to learn that you are tense; you know it already. Why else would you want to learn to relax; why would you be reading this book? You know that you are tense because you experience the unpleasant results of tension—the effect—but you have never learned to recognize the cause and, therefore, have not been able to deal with it properly. Daily practice with the formula gives us the experience of knowing what tension is in a very personal and intimate way. When we know exactly what it is, the ability to relax becomes practically automatic.

How Our Muscles Work

It is not necessary to be a student of anatomy, to know the names of the different muscles, their location and functions, in order to learn to relax. However, a little knowledge of the way your muscles function may help you to recognize what you are doing when you are tense, and stop doing it.

The muscles in the front of your neck pull the head forward; the muscles along the back of the neck pull the head backward; the muscles along the left side of the neck pull the head to the left. The muscles along the back of the trunk pull the trunk backward in relation to the legs; they hold the body erect, and lift it from a bent-over position. The abdomen muscles in the front of the body pull the trunk forward in relation to the legs; they do the work when you sit up, after you have been lying down. The deltoid muscle on top of the shoulder pulls the arm outward and upward. The muscle in your side, underneath the armpit, pulls the arm downward to the side. The biceps muscle in the front of the upper arm brings the hand upward toward the shoulder. The triceps muscle in the back of the upper arm straightens out, or pushes, the arm to a straight position. Remember that the muscle is always on the inside of the arc of the movement it initiates. The muscles in the inside of your fingers, hand, wrist and forearm bring the fingers in toward these muscles when you grip. The muscles in the back of the hand, and the top of the forearm, extend the fingers and bring them up and backward toward these muscles.

If you will remember these simple facts about your muscles, you will be helped, at the beginning, to relieve tension. For example, when you feel tension in the back of your neck, you know that you are trying to pull the head backward. To stop tensing these muscles, you merely stop trying to pull the head backward. When you feel tension in the muscles of your jaw, what you are really trying to do is to bring your teeth together tightly. The only way to relax is to stop trying to clench your teeth.

Do not think that you must spend the rest of your life continually looking for tension in your muscles. At first, the recognition of tension and the dropping of it must be a deliberate, conscious act. But with practice, relaxation tends to become habitual. The more you practice, the more tension tends to become conscious, and relaxation unconscious. Finally, you reach the ideal: tension is entirely conscious and intentional—that is, your muscles do not contract except when you intend them to, when such contractions are needed for purposeful action —and, at the same time, relaxation becomes almost entirely automatic and habitual. Nor does this intentional contraction of muscles mean that you must give conscious, painstaking thought to each muscular movement. When we learn relaxation, our muscles perform purposeful and directed actions with a minimum of waste motion and with a minimum of conscious attention.

My experience has been that until such time as we really learn to be completely relaxed, daily practice in the use of the formula is necessary in order to maintain our degree of skill or to improve it. But once we have learned relaxation completely, which is the same as saying that we have learned perfect control of our muscles, daily practice is no longer needed. We can forget about it, and we will find that we will be automatically relaxed as we go about our daily tasks. It seems to be a truism that we can forget about and put behind us those things we have mastered, conquered or learned thoroughly. We can then be free to learn something else.

Recently, I met a man whom I had taught to relax about eight years before. While he was learning to relax, he had religiously set aside a period each day for practice. He had not been content with partial relief from tension; he stuck with it until he had mastered it. When I met him he told me that he had not practiced the formula for over six years. Indeed, he had even forgotten the specific details of the formula. But he had acquired a relief from tension that had stayed with him through some trying experiences.

This forgetting of the details of learning is also characteristic of complete learning. A good golfer doesn't really know what it is he is doing when he performs all the details of a good swing. He has forgotten; he just does it. Try to explain to someone just exactly what it is you do subjectively when you perform some simple task like walking. You will find it difficult, if not impossible, because you forgot long ago just how you mentally command your legs to walk—you just walk. You have forgotten, but your leg muscles remember. Try to explain to someone just what it is you do with your throat muscles and tongue and lips when you talk, and you are apt to find yourself in the position of the old man who was asked by his grandson: "Grandpa, do you sleep with your long beard on the outside or the inside of the covers?" The old man had slept soundly for seventy-five years, but that night he couldn't sleep. He was too busy trying to remember just how he did sleep.

Just as you do not now have to give any special thought or conscious attention to being tense all day, you will soon substitute the habit of relaxation for the habit of tension, and it will require just as little attention on your part, after you have learned relaxation completely and thoroughly.

Chapter Four

Reducing the Breathing Cycle

There is a definite correlation between breathing and mental and emotional activity. When we are emotionally tense, we have something on our chests, and we all know the relief of getting it off our chests. When a crisis is past, and we feel we can afford to relax, we say that we can breathe easier.

But it works both ways. If we can learn to breathe easier in the first place, we won't get so tense. And if we begin deliberately to breathe easier when we are feeling tense, the tension begins to flow out of us.

Most nervous people hyper-ventilate. They breathe too fast and too deeply. They take into their bodies an excess of oxygen which, in turn, causes the metabolic fires of the body to burn too brightly. This hyper-ventilation gears up the body's physiological process to a high pitch which adds to the feeling of nervousness.

If you are about to use your muscles strenuously, hyper-ventilation is a good thing. Most weight lifters deliberately hyper-ventilate just before lifting a very heavy weight, by taking a number of quick, deep breaths. If you are about to try to break the world's record in the two-hands press, or the hundred-yard dash, or if you are about to unload a truck of heavy packing cases, hyper-ventilation will help you. If you suddenly come upon a bear in the woods, you need to hyper-ventilate. And you will do so automatically, without having to give any thought to the matter. It is nature's way of gearing your body for a fast get-away.

Hyper-ventilation is a stimulant for your physical mechanism. It enables you to make greater efforts with your muscles, not with your mind. In an emergency, such as meeting a bear in the woods, or a near miss on the highway, thinking seems to be temporarily suspended. It is not until later that you can realize fully just what you did and why you did it.

It requires effort to lift a heavy weight, or to run a hundred-yard dash. But it requires no conscious, physical effort to think, to see, to hear, or to remember. When we attempt to use effort in a situation where it *cannot* be used, and therefore where there is no channel for its release, it remains bottled up inside us to make us nervous and tense.

Think about the actions of a man about to make a speech. He begins to breathe faster, just as if he were about to use his muscles to fight a bear. The actual job of making a speech calls for no such strenuous expenditure of muscular energy. The amount of tension he has built up in his chest has no way of being used up. His chest begins to feel tight and he gets "butterflies in his stomach." Instinctively, he feels compelled to drain off some of this excess energy so he begins to fidget. He paces back and forth; he drums on the table; he sits down; but he cannot sit still. His body is trying to help him to get rid of the tension in the only way he can use it—through his muscles. But he need never have built it up in the first place. There is no need to get tense and excited about getting your message across. You can't get it across with your muscles. If there is anything in your mind worth saying, it will come out—if you relax and let it. If it isn't there, straining won't put it there, so in either case, why worry about it?

Many nervous people go through the entire day with a sort of chronic case of stage fright. They have so exaggerated and misinterpreted the amount of effort required to do even routine jobs that they keep themselves geared up as if they were to compete in a foot race. Learning to deliberately breathe slower can help us overcome this.

You can learn to breathe easier just as you learn any other habit, by practicing calm, serene, relaxed breathing. If, when you find yourself breathing nervously and jerkily, you draw yourself up short, so to speak, and sit down and begin to breathe calmly, your subconscious will soon catch on and form the habit. Don't *make* yourself breathe easier—*let* yourself do it. If you push a dog down persistently each time he tries to jump up on you, he will, in time, learn to stop doing it. Your body can be trained in the same way.

It will also help you if you learn to evaluate situations correctly. Keep reminding yourself that effort is for muscles. Effort is a mental demand upon your muscles. If you mistakenly conceive of a situation as calling for effort, your subconscious will make you breathe faster, and will charge your muscles with an overload of energy. You decide, by the way you interpret a situation, whether your subconscious will call up reinforcements or not. If you become firmly convinced that effort is for muscular action only, that a particular situation does not require strenuous muscular action, and that there is nothing you can do about it with your muscles, your subconscious will not call up reinforcements, will not make you breathe faster.

Hyper-ventilation is good just before, during, and immediately after muscular exercise. At other times it is like building a big fire under the boiler when there is no outlet for the steam pressure. Keeping the body continually geared up for action is a tremendous waste of energy and vitality.

Full breathing is necessary for health, and as long as the rhythm is smooth, and not too fast and jerky, so-called deep breathing can actually have a relaxing effect upon the body while we are active. But full, relaxed, deep breathing is different from forced deep breathing. Breathing deeply and smoothly, with a relaxed rhythm, aids the circulation of the blood, and helps the muscles and physical sense organs to relax. Prove this to yourself sometime when your eyes feel strained and the print you are reading becomes blurred. Close your eyes, take a deep breath, and let it out with a relaxed sigh. Then

open our eyes and you will find that the print has cleared
—unless there is something actually wrong with your
eyes, in which case, of course, you should see your eye
doctor.

If you find yourself breathing nervously and fast and
cannot seem to slow down your breathing without a feeling of effort, do not attempt to lower your breathing rate
immediately. Do not make efforts and put your conscious
will in direct opposition to your subconscious. Instead,
go along with your subconscious for a little while. Remember that effort increases both emotion and tension.
If you make an effort to stop breathing fast, you will only
add fuel to the emotional fires, which in turn will make
you want to breathe even faster. If you wish to stop a
runaway horse you do not stand directly in his path and
attempt to block him. Instead, you ride alongside, going
in the same direction he is going, grasp his reins, and
gradually slow him up. Your conscious will can use a
similar technique for taming your runaway subconscious.

The way to do this is to begin to breathe fast and
jerkily, consciously and deliberately. Keep right on
breathing as you were before—but now breathe that
way because that is the way you *want* to breathe. Take
as many as fifty to a hundred of these deliberate nervous
breaths, thus bringing your breathing under the control of your will. This in itself will cause the subjective
feeling of nervousness to diminish. We do not feel nervous, tense, and uncomfortable, when we are exercis-
ing mental control of our muscles. So, begin to calm

down by consciously co-operating with your fast breathing. After a time you will find that the inner compulsion to breathe fast has either disappeared entirely or has greatly diminished. You will then feel that it is an effort and a chore to keep breathing fast, and a relief to stop and just let yourself breathe more slowly. The slower rate will then seem natural and unforced. You can now stop doing it consciously and your subconscious will take over at the slower rate.

If you have ever been on a crowded bus or subway train, you have no doubt noticed that a number of people seem to become very drowsy and relaxed. Perhaps you have had a similar experience yourself. The reason for this is that the amount of oxygen in the air of a crowded bus is somewhat lower in proportion to the carbon dioxide than it would be in a less crowded place. I do not recommend living in poorly ventilated quarters. We cannot live without oxygen; it is necessary for life and health. But there can be too much of even a good thing. If you are habitually nervous and high strung, the chances are that you are taking in more oxygen than your body can use.

Dr. L. J. Meduna, Professor of Psychiatry at the College of Medicine of the University of Illinois, has developed what he calls "Carbon Dioxide Therapy," based upon the fact that inhalation of carbon dioxide gas decreases the excitability of the nerve cells in the brain. Dr. Meduna has used this method to help nervous, neurotic patients overcome anxiety, depression, stuttering, and other psychosomatic ills.

Sir William Osler, in his *Principles and Practice of Medicine* (Appleton-Century-Crofts, New York), notes that excessive breathing causes nervousness and alkalosis, and that efforts should be made to reduce this excessive breathing by having the patient breathe through a tube, and rebreathe into a gas bag; or by administering oxygen-carbon-dioxide mixture.

We accomplish the same result when we learn to breathe slower and more serenely. Oxygen keeps the fires of the body burning. But if we have the fires turned up so high that there is an excess of pressure in the boiler, we need to turn them down a bit. And when the time comes for complete passive relaxation, we need to bank those fires, and turn them down even lower. That is what we do in step two of the formula.

Because breathing is one bodily function that is under the control of both the voluntary and involuntary nervous systems, and because it is tied in with all other involuntary organic processes, breathing furnishes us with a valuable control knob for toning down the degree of excitement throughout the entire body. Your viscera, for example, cannot be churning with nervous excitement when your breathing is calm and relaxed.

The Two Ways of Breathing

It will help you to learn to breathe correctly if you recognize that your body has two separate breathing patterns.

Nervous breathers breathe high in the chest by expanding and contracting the rib box. This particular breathing pattern was engineered for fast and furious breathing. It is the way you breathe when you are all out of breath from running a race. Watch a man after strenuous exertion, and you will notice how his chest heaves as he takes in great gulps of air. An emergency exists. His muscles need oxygen fast, and this is the fastest way to get it. This is also the way you breathe just before muscular effort, when you are excited and your subconscious supplies you with an additional shot of oxygen in a hurry.

Nervous, tense hyper-ventilators have gotten so used to nervousness, anxiety, and the mistaken idea that emergency behavior is required for simple, ordinary tasks, that they use their emergency breathing mechanism all the time

Non-emergency breathing is done from the diaphragm. Most of the movement is in the lower chest wall and the upper abdomen. While the diaphragm muscle is used in all breathing, this non-emergency breathing is usually spoken of as breathing from the diaphragm, or belly breathing. It is virtually impossible to feel nervous and tense when you breathe habitually from your diaphragm. As the diaphragm gently, smoothly and rhythmically contracts and lets go, a gentle massage is applied to the whole abdominal area. You cannot hold your abdominal muscles tense and rigid and do belly breathing.

Rigidity of the abdominal muscles is natural with high chest breathing. High chest breathing is emergency behavior, during which the whole body is geared up for defense and attack. The abdominal muscles instinctively tighten, as a defensive measure, as if to ward off blows. The normal activities of the stomach itself are temporarily shut down, to furnish more blood and energy to the muscles, which may explain why nervous chest-breathers nearly always have digestive troubles. During an emergency, the adrenal glands pour an additional shot of adrenalin into the blood to stimulate the muscles still further. The whole physical and mental mechanism is alerted for danger, which may help explain why chest breathers complain of fatigue and exhaustion, and have trouble relaxing or going to sleep.

A whole vicious cycle of tension is set up when a person is habitually on the defensive, over-alert for dangers that aren't there. The breathing cycle is an important link in this chain or cycle of tension. By removing one link in the defensive-tension cycle, we break the entire cycle. That is the reason I have made reduction of the breathing cycle step two of my formula for passive relaxation.

Relaxed breathing enables you not only to relax faster and go to sleep quicker when lying down, but can also help you to relax and feel better all through the day.

Remember these things:

1. Do not wait to breathe easier until everything is all right and you can afford to relax. Learn to breathe easier first, and you will find yourself more relaxed.

2. Learn the habit of serene, relaxed breathing and of breathing a little slower. Normal breathing cycles vary with individuals. Generally, there are about 18 or 20 inhalations per minute when you are normally active, but not doing anything really strenuous, and from 10 to 14 inhalations per minute when you are passively relaxing.

3. Learn to interpret situations better, and realize which ones call for muscular effort and which ones do not. If the situation does not call for a muscular solution, relax away any temptation to try to do something with your muscles. This will help keep your breathing relaxed.

4. Practice belly breathing until it becomes habitual.

Chapter Five

Mental Imagery

Muscular contraction is one link in the chain of tension. Mental imagery is another link. In order to break the vicious cycle of tension it is really necessary to remove only one link. However, it has been my experience that most people progress faster if an attack is made simultaneously on both of these links in the chain of tension.

When you are practicing passive relaxation, be willing to give up the desire to be doing something. Trying to relax when you are in a hurry, or when you have a sneaking suspicion that you ought to be up and doing, presents two conflicting mental images, both of which your muscles try to obey. For this reason I always advise students, especially when they first begin learning relaxation, to decide beforehand that they intend to spend a certain amount of time each day (if possible at the same time each day), practicing relaxation and doing nothing else. Make an appointment with yourself. And make up your mind in advance that regardless of the amount of progress you seem to be making, you will spend the entire time doing nothing but practicing relaxation. Agree with yourself in advance that you are going to invest this time in relaxation. Realize that it is not time lost, but probably one of the best uses you could be making of that particular time. You will then approach your relaxation period with no feeling that you ought to be doing something else.

I once knew a man who could relax perfectly when getting a haircut and shave in the barber shop, who found it impossible to relax at home in an easy chair, or in his bed at night. He even purchased a barber chair and had it installed in his home, but this didn't solve his problem. He could still relax only in the barber shop. When he told me about this I suggested that it was not the place, but his own attitude that enabled him to relax. This man was a typical high-powered executive who felt he should be forever up and doing. His conscience bothered him when he tried to relax at home or at the office. He felt unconsciously that he was wasting good time that he could be putting to more profitable use. There was always the possibility that he could be doing something else instead. When he went to the barber shop, this possibility of doing something else was entirely removed. A man cannot dictate letters, work on reports, and make long-distance telephone calls while getting a shave. When he entered the barber shop he gave up even the possibility of doing anything else. He realized that he was going to spend a certain amount of time during which he could do nothing but get a shave and haircut. This created the ideal mental setup for relaxation.

When I made him realize this, he was able to relax at home simply by telling himself that a period of relaxation was every bit as important to him as a haircut, and that he was going to spend half an hour in his easy chair or bed, during which time he would absolutely forbid himself to do anything else, regardless of the temptation to get up. As soon as he made it impossible for himself to do anything else, he was able to relax.

Good and Bad Mental Images

What you look at mentally has a powerful effect upon your body. Many people are sickened by the sight of blood. Others will shiver with revulsion or tremble in fear when someone is describing a frightful or horrible experience. Worry and emotional tension are always accompanied by unpleasant mental pictures. Pleasant mental images require less effort, cause less strain and contraction than unpleasant ones.

Psychologist K. Kekcheyev tested patients when they were thinking pleasant thoughts and also when they were thinking unpleasant thoughts. He found that when they were thinking pleasant thoughts all their physical senses were more acute. They could see, hear, taste, and smell better, and their sense of touch was more keen.

Many years ago, Dr. William H. Bates, a well-known ophthalmologist, stated that all functional eye troubles were caused by mental strain and by making an effort to see. The highest degree of refractive error could be relieved in a fraction of a second, he said, when the eye and mind were perfectly relaxed. A New York optometrist, Leon Gordon, has had almost complete success in relieving myopia at his Myopia Control Foundation, with a system of treatment that is aimed at relieving emotional tensions.

Whatever helps you to see better, hear better, or think better, also helps you to relax, because relaxation and proper functioning go together.

Aldous Huxley, in his book, *The Art of Seeing* (Harper and Brothers, New York), tells how daily practice in visualizing pleasant mental pictures helped him to relax his mind and improve his eyesight.

I do not believe that one can or should ignore unpleasant realities. But the pleasant things in life are as real as the unpleasant ones. We are not necessarily dodging reality when we contemplate pleasant mental pictures. The chronic worrier is a person who has placed too much emphasis on the unpleasant things, and because he has over-emphasized the pessimistic side of his nature, he is as unrealistic as the bright-eyed optimist he so despises. Spending eight hours a day dealing realistically with the unpleasant aspects of life is quite enough, it seems to me. In our hours of rest and recreation, and especially just before retiring at night, we should emphasize the pleasant. Do not be afraid of being called an escapist. Sleep itself is an escape, and has been wisely provided by nature because we need it. Many people take their business worries home with them, and rob their hours of recreation of the pleasure and restorative value they should have. When they get into bed they continue to look mentally at all the troubles of yesterday, today and tomorrow.

A minister once told me that he completely cured himself of insomnia when he realized the childishness and futility of allowing to pass in review mentally, after he had gone to bed, all his problems of the day and all the problems he would be likely to face the next day. He said that one night he suddenly realized that there was nothing in the world that he could do while in bed at night that would help him solve any of his problems. So he decided: "I will just say my prayers, refuse to look at my worries, and go to sleep. I go to bed for just one purpose and that is to go to sleep; therefore, I will not try to do anything else."

Relax Away Worry

A knowledge of mental imagery and the way it works also enables us to deal with worry. The chronic worrier indulges in negative, painful, unpleasant mental images. He is forever holding before his mind the pictures of what he doesn't want to happen. The creative thinker goes through the same motions as the worrier. But he holds before his mind pictures of things that he wants to accomplish, what he does want to happen.

In one of the best books on the subject of worry that I have ever seen, *In the Name of Common Sense*

(The Macmillan Company, New York), Matthew N. Chappell, Ph. D., says that the practice of substituting pleasant mental pictures for unpleasant ones is the best technique that psychology has yet discovered for combating worry. Dr. Chappell points out that this technique of substituting pleasant images for unpleasant ones does far more than furnish an escape for the mind. It also reduces excess emotion, as well as excess effort, both of which are component parts of worry. He says that if you attempt to use will power against your worries you only worry more, for your additional effort increases the emotional tone. Instead, you should make no effort whatsoever to fight worry. Relax from trying. For a period of several weeks, make it a practice to draw yourself up short whenever you start to worry, and realize that you are picturing unpleasant mental images. When you do realize this, then deliberately begin to picture pleasant mental images.

Dr. Chappell recommends that you do not wait until you are worrying to decide upon a pleasant mental picture. Decide on one in advance so that you will have it ready for use in emergencies. Remember some pleasant incident in your childhood that you can call up when needed—a picnic, the day you won the race at school, your first dance, a fishing trip—anything at all that has pleasant associations. After you practice this for several weeks you break the worry habit.

Don't resist your unpleasant mental images with will power. Don't bother with them at all. Just leave them alone and focus your attention deliberately upon some pleasant memory. Another famous psychologist, David Seabury, recommends the same technique as one of the best ways to overcome neurotic anxiety. Every time you are in a situation that tempts you to worry, he says, substitute positive, wholesome images instead, and in time the very situation that acted as a trigger on your anxiety will become a conditioned stimulus for calm, collected, creative thought.

A "Swing" That Relaxes Eyes and Mind

Anything that relaxes the eyes also relaxes the mind, and helps to bring mental imagery under control. A movement that is very valuable for teaching rhythmic relaxation to the eyes is called "the swing." Besides teaching your eyes to function in a relaxed manner, the swing is very valuable in teaching your whole body to function with rhythmic relaxation.

Stand in the center of a room, with feet approximately 18 inches apart, and with the hands hanging loosely at the sides. Do not turn your head upon your neck, and don't twist your shoulders during the entire movement. All the movement is from the hips and waist. Slowly turn your *whole upper body* to the left, until you are looking at the left wall of the room. As you turn to the left, raise your right heel from the floor, and bend the right knee slightly. The hands are allowed to hang loosely at the sides as if they were two dead weights tied to the shoulders by ropes. When you have completed the left turn, slowly turn back to the right until you are facing the right wall, lifting the left heel from the floor as you turn, and bending the left knee slightly. This is *not* a calisthenic exercise. It is not to be performed energetically, but smoothly, rhythmically, and even somewhat lazily. As you turn back and forth, your hands should flop back and forth without any will on your part. Do not attempt to focus on objects as they go by you. Do not try to see individual objects clearly; let them go by in a blur. After a few swings, you will get the sensation that the objects in the room are going past you in the opposite direction of your swing. When this happens, it means that your eyes are no longer staring, and are letting the objects flow by. From 60 to 100 complete swings should be performed at one practice session, at the rate of about 16 swings a minute.

This exercise forces the eyes to give up their strained trying and to move with rhythmic relaxation. It is also valuable for the shoulders, arms, spine and, in fact, for the entire body. One hundred swings a day will be a valuable aid in helping you to acquire the habit of rhythmic relaxation, and if performed just before retiring, will insure that you go to bed with your eyes relaxed. It is always easier to proceed to passive relaxation from rhythmic relaxation than to try to go from a state of tense functioning to passive relaxation.

An Image to Relax Your Mind

In the Formula for Passive Relaxation, we make use of another device for starting the eyes and mind on the road to relaxation. This device can be used when you are sitting or lying down, with the eyes closed. It is the simple device of visualizing or remembering black.

Dr. Bates discovered that as long as his patients were either visualizing, imagining, or remembering a small black period, their eyes were relaxed, there was no effort or strain, and refractive errors that might be present were temporarily corrected as long as the eyes and mind remained relaxed.

The reason that visualizing a black period brings mental and eye relaxation is this: you cannot remember or mentally visualize anything perfectly when the mind or the eyes are tense. Both memory and vision work at their optimum when the mind and the eyes are relaxed. The black period does not make you relax. But while you are visualizing or remembering it you are relaxed. If you succeed in visualizing it, you know your eyes and your mind are relaxed.

If the average patient is told to relax his mind, he has no idea what he is supposed to do. If he is told to remember a small black period, he is given something definite to do, that is easy to do, and in doing it he brings about the mental attitude that is necessary for relaxation.

Do not try to see a black period. Do not try to imagine that you see one objectively on some physical object such as a sheet of paper. Just remember having seen one, and you will be visualizing it correctly. Remembering *any* black object is relaxing to the eyes and the seeing mind behind the eyes. Some people can remember a black object such as a telephone, a pair of black shoes, or a lump of black coal, more easily than they can remember a period. Some can remember a comma, a semicolon or a colon better than a period. Remember any small black object that is easy for you to remember.

Sometimes, remembering a small black period, or a small black letter, is easier if you remember having seen it in some specific book, newspaper, or other printed matter. Try typing a black period on a small calling card, in the very center of the card. Look at the card casually once a day. Later on in the day, remember having looked at the card; remember where you were; recall taking the card from your pocket and remember the way the period on it looked to you at the time.

When you feel the pressure on, when you are in a pinch or a tight place, the use of the black period, or other small black object, affords you a ready antidote to tension. Dr. Bates recommended carrying the image of a black period around with you in the back of your mind. In this way you keep your mental faculties focused, so to speak, and relaxed. Dr. Bates said that whenever he could not remember the name of a patient readily, he would not try to remember the name, but would visualize the black period instead. This relaxed his mind, allowed his memory to work for him, and the name popped into his mind.

The use of this black period, or other appropriate black object, can also be of great help to us in carrying our relaxed attitude with us as we go out and engage in the various activities of the day. This, of course, should be one of the aims of any relaxation program. But when we become involved in activity, we cannot always be sure whether or not we are remaining relaxed. If you can remember the black period, you know you are maintaining your rhythmic relaxation.

When you are calling on an important customer, when you are up at bat and the count is two strikes and three balls, any time when you feel pressured or harassed or hurried, stop and take a mental look at the black period.

Do not expect to be able to do this perfectly at first, and do not become discouraged when you fail. Just keep it in mind as your ultimate goal—and little by little you will approach it. Have a relaxed attitude about this, as about everything else. Be more or less indifferent to results and you will progress better. The fate of the world does not hinge upon your being able to do it the first time, or the fifth. Persistence will eventually bring success. Approach the whole subject in the spirit of a game —not as if it were a life or death struggle.

In the meantime, glance casually at the figures below, then close the book and see how easy it is for you to remember them. Some people can remember better if their motor mechanism is involved. If this is true of you, try drawing your own figures, invent new ones, and see if this helps you to remember them better.

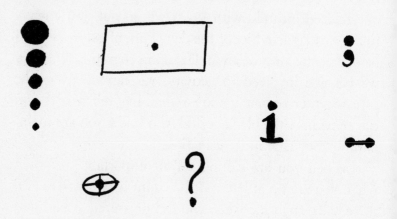

Chapter Six

Key Points for Relaxation

While serving in the Hospital Corps of the Navy I sat in on and assisted in many surgical operations. After seeing countless men put under an anaesthetic, I learned that you could predict in advance those who would go under easily, those who would let go and surrender themselves to the doctor and the anaesthetist, and those who would be hard to put to sleep. All you had to do was look at the man's hands. If they were folded quietly in repose, he would make a good patient. But if they were tense, fingers extended and stiff, or balled into fists, we always had a fight on our hands to get him to sleep.

The Hands

The hands are the main executive instrument of the body. They are involved, perhaps more directly than any other part of the body, in our doing. Our hands are used to express our emotions and inner feelings. When we are angry, we shake our fist or shake our finger in our enemy's face. We make threatening gestures, and bang the table for emphasis. We throw up our hands in hopelessness, wash our hands of guilt, let a situation or problem pass out of our hands.

Tense hands are geared for doing. And when the hands are kept tense, the whole body is geared for doing. When our hands have work to do, and we contract the muscles in the hands just enough to get the job done, that is good. But when we are waiting for a bus to arrive, or hoping that a boring speaker will hurry and finish his speech, or when we are in the midst of any other common annoying situation, we need to realize that there is nothing we can do with our hands to solve these problems. Unless our hands themselves are involved in the actual job that is being done, we should keep them relaxed. And when they are involved in doing, we should not contract them more than necessary. Most people grip a pen or pencil with about ten times the contraction that is required for the job. We hang on to things for dear life, as if we were hanging over a precipice by our fingertips.

A stenographer told me that typing made the back of her neck hurt and gave her headaches. I watched her type and noticed that she held her hands and fingers tense—as if her fingers were claws and she were about to attack the typewriter. She herself had never noticed this, until it was called to her attention. What she noticed was the ill-at-ease feeling, the ache in the back of her neck and her headaches. By consciously and deliberately recognizing the tension in her fingers and hands and dropping it, she not only found her work less tiring, but her headaches and neck aches disappeared.

In most sports, a firm and commanding grip upon some instrument is necessary for good performance. But even here we can overdo it. A golfer and a baseball batter both need a firm grip. But one of the characteristics of blowing up in either baseball or golf is excess gripping power. When the pressure is on in a golf match, when you just have to make a good shot, or just after you have made a bad one, forego the temptation to grip the club tighter. Most golfers blow up when they find themselves in a difficult situation. Then they mistakenly and unconsciously reason that this calls for excess contraction, that they can get themselves out of the difficulty by doing more with their muscles. They grip the shaft until the knuckles are white. But this excess contraction serves only to increase the feeling of difficulty and inadequacy. It also upsets the natural rhythm of their stroking, they make another poor shot, and find themselves in still worse difficulty. Now they make even greater efforts, make more unnecessary contractions, further foul up their rhythmic grooves, and suddenly find their game completely shot.

Pretty much the same thing happens to a baseball player in a batting slump.

Learn to relax your hands a little when you find yourself in a tight spot. It will take the pressure off— and give you the feeling that you are master of the situation.

In my work with young inexperienced pilots I discovered that they would grip the controls so tightly that they suffered from aches and cramps in their hands. This overcontraction also upset their physical reflexes. When they were taught to relax their hands, and let the ship fly itself, instead of unconsciously trying to propel it with their own hand strength, their reflexes returned, their flying became smoother, and they gained a sense of mastery over the ship.

In the game of life, as well as in sports, the skilled performer is the one who handles the controls with a light touch.

The Brow

The muscles of the brow and forehead are closely associated with worry, anxiety, consternation and confusion. The poet speaks of the brow being wrinkled with care. When the novelist wants to show us that a character is worried or displeased, he tells us that he frowns.

In a book called *Expression of the Emotions in Man and Animals* (Thinker's Library, British Book Center, New York), Charles Darwin pointed out that frowning is the physical expression of a feeling that there is some difficulty to be overcome. He said: "We have seen that frowning is the natural expression of some difficulty encountered, or of something disagreeable experienced either in thought or action, and he whose mind is often and readily affected in this way, will be apt to be ill-tempered, or slightly angry, or peevish, and will commonly show it by frowning."

About the time that Darwin wrote this, William James was also developing his theory about emotions. He said that in order to feel a certain emotion our muscles must first do certain things, that the feeling of an emotion and the physical expression of it are welded together.

With the brow relaxed it is practically impossible to feel worried. Most people do not realize that they could relieve themselves considerably of feelings of pressure and difficulty by the simple expedient of relaxing the brow and forehead. The next time you have a problem to solve, make it a point to keep your brow relaxed, and see if it is not true that with the forehead relaxed the problem will not seem so difficult. You can then study it with calm deliberation. Another good reason for keeping your brows smooth is that you will have the appearance of poise and ease, and will give a good impression of yourself to others.

The Jaw

The jaw is one of the most expressive parts of the human body. We grit our teeth in rage. We also clench our jaws in determination. The jaw is probably the best thermometer, or gauge, of the tense person. If you are habitually tense, if you are guilty of making excess efforts, if you are over-determined, it shows up in your jaw.

There are times when we need to be determined, of course. But determination is not required of us every minute of the day, in every task or movement. When your jaw is tensed, your mid-brain, which is constantly receiving nerve messages from your muscles, reasons something like this: "We must be in difficulty, we must be facing insurmountable obstacles, we must have a terrible job to do, and victory must be somewhat in doubt; otherwise, why all this iron-jawed determination?" The mid-brain is convinced you are in a difficult situation. Then you become conscious of a feeling of anxiety, of inadequacy, of pressure. Just as soon as you relax your jaw muscles, ease up on your iron-jawed determination, your mid-brain says: "Ah, we are out of the difficulty now. We are well able to handle this situation. The obstacles that face us must not be so great after all." You get a feeling of confidence—the pressure, hurry, and sense of immediacy and emergency subside, and you find yourself more the master of the situation.

Every time you feel hurried, every time you feel inadequate, every time you experience self-doubt or anxiety about results, stop and deliberately notice that you are contracting your jaws; then stop doing it.

A little determination is good. But a little self-confidence is still better. And over-determination implies a certain lack of self-confidence in your ability to do whatever needs to be done.

The Abdomen

When I was physical-training instructor at Bill Brown's Health Farm, I was amazed at the number of business executives who suffered from spastic colon. Of course, you cannot relax the colon directly, in the way that you can relax your biceps. But studies made by experts, and my own experiences, have shown that when the skeletal muscles in a certain area of the body are relaxed and kept relaxed, the organs in the same area have a tendency to relax by a sort of reflex action. Whatever the cause of spastic colon may be, actual experiments have shown that when you learn to relax your abdominal area, the spastic colon seems to cure itself.

Over-protectiveness, an exaggerated defensive attitude toward life in general, is characteristic of tenseness. The tense person feels subconsciously that he cannot trust life. He must keep himself ever alert, ever on the defensive, in case something should happen. He is a little bit afraid to trust the chair to hold him up. He holds his head as if he were afraid it might fall off if he dared let go. He carries his shoulders hunched and ready—as if to ward off unexpected blows.

This defensive attitude explains why many people go around all the time with their midsection unconsciously tensed. If you are expecting a blow at the pit of the stomach, you instinctively tense the abdominal muscles for protection. And if you habitually live on the defensive, your subconscious keeps your stomach muscles continuously tensed. This may explain the remark so many people make when they hear bad news: "It hit me right in the pit of my stomach."

I know that life is not a bed of roses. I also know that no amount of planning and foresight can rule out the possibility of some unexpected bad news. But to over-respond to trouble, and to be continually over-mobilized against it, is as bad as no preparedness at all. If we could maintain some basic trust in life that would enable us to relax our over-defensiveness, we would be better able to deal with the difficult situations when and if they do arise. An army wouldn't last long if all its reserves were kept rigidly at attention twenty-four hours a day.

When we go around with our abdominal muscles continually tensed, we again set up a vicious cycle. We keep them tense because we feel insecure, and keeping them tense reinforces our feeling of insecurity. The mid-brain receives messages from the muscles as well as the muscles from the mid-brain. If we can break the cycle at any point, we can stop the subjective feelings of in-security and anxiety, and at the same time allow our internal organs to perform their work without undue pressure and strain.

When you feel insecure and anxious, notice the muscles of your abdominal area. The chances are that they will be tense and rigid. Stop right then and make them relax. If you practice this regularly, eventually you will find that you feel better both physically and mentally.

How to Relax the Key Areas

To obtain the most good from relaxation, you should have at least one period each day of passive relaxation, with someone to read the formula to you. This daily practice is very important. You are in effect learning a new habit—the habit of relaxation. Continual daily practice in passive relaxation will set up a habitual pattern that will carry over unconsciously into your daily activities.

But this habitual relaxation can be facilitated by your making regular checks at other times during the day on your key points. Don't try to watch yourself continuously. Don't make a project out of it. Check over your key points quickly at mid-morning, just before lunch, and in mid-afternoon. At other times, forget about them, unless you catch yourself tensing up in some act, such as gripping the pen you are writing with, or because something unpleasant has happened. If something has made you angry, or if someone keeps you waiting for an appointment, or if you miss your train (or think you're about to), or you have to wait a while for service in the restaurant at lunch time, you'll no doubt begin to tense up at some or all of your key points. Check them, then. Even the act of checking over them will help you to relax, because you'll be thinking about your muscles, and about untensing them, instead of thinking about the thing that upset you. By the time you finish your check-up, the waitress, or the man you had an appointment with, will probably have turned up, and that crisis will be past—and you'll be wondering why you made a fuss about it in the first place.

We use a little different technique for relaxing the key points during the day than in the regular passive relaxation periods. The underlying method is the same, but we approach it a little differently.

Experience has shown that nearly everyone will make some sort of effort when attempting relaxation alone. This is the reason we are so insistent upon having someone read the instructions on passive relaxation to you. But what do you do during the day, when you want to relax your key points and you have no one to read instructions to you?

Simply this: whether or not you realize it, the chances are about 99 in a hundred that instinctively you are going to make some sort of effort when you try to relax by yourself. If you do make an effort to relax, you will defeat your purpose. So we take that old enemy, effort, and use him for our own purposes. We will make a conscious effort to *tense* the key points. It is a sort of jujitsu principle that we use—employ the strength of your enemy in order to make him throw himself.

Quickly go over your key points and see if there is any excess tension at any one of them. Until you have learned to relax completely, there will always be excess tension in your body, but it is unconscious tension until you notice it. The first step is to notice it by making it conscious instead of unconscious tension. The next step is to remind yourself that you are the one who is causing your muscles to tense. Say something like this to yourself: "My jaws are not clenching themselves. I am doing something to make my jaws clench. I am now going to practice consciously what I have been doing unconsciously."

Then proceed, consciously and deliberately, to clench your teeth together. Make an effort to tense your key areas and pay attention to what you are doing when you tense them. Say to yourself: "This is what I have been doing to make me so tense." Tense the key areas from ten to twenty-five times—each time tensing them a little less and a little less, but still paying conscious attention to what you are doing. Then, when you are through making efforts to be tense, just say to yourself: "Now I have finished that exercise—I am through doing that for this time." *That* is relaxation. And it requires no more effort than *not* climbing a flight of stairs, or *not* running the hundred-yard dash. When you stop doing what you had been doing, you will be relaxing without having made any conscious effort to do so.

Our muscles are controlled by both our voluntary and our involuntary nervous systems. When we perform an act so many times that it requires no conscious attention, it is performed by the involuntary nervous system and becomes a habit. Tension is a habit with most people. It goes on unconsciously and without our volition.

If we begin to practice it consciously, we bring it out of the habit class and begin to practice controlling it with our voluntary nervous system—our will. And when we have learned to control tension, we can turn it off or on at will. When we have learned perfect control, we just never bother to turn it on any more.

When you tense a muscle because you want to, you experience none of the unpleasant subjective effects of unconscious tension, such as nervousness, fidgety feelings, or restlessness.

After your daily practice periods in contracting your key points, the muscles in these areas will have a natural tendency to relax of their own accord, and without your giving them any thought, because it is a physiological fact that a period of relaxation naturally follows a period of contraction.

This technique of deliberate tensing of muscles is also useful because it enables you to practice something you already know how to do. This is important, because many people become anxious and tense when they think about trying to relax; they think they are being asked to do something that they know nothing about. Yet, all your life you have been trained to make efforts, you know what that means, and you know it is nothing to get anxious or excited about.

You should go through this daily practice as impersonally and objectively as possible. Practice learning control of your body in much the same way that you would go about learning the control of a piano keyboard. Go through this daily practice in deliberately making yourself tense without concerning yourself about results, and in a month or six weeks you will find that something has happened—you will find that you are not as tense and nervous as you were. The times when you feel relaxed will have become more frequent and more continuous. In short, you will have made considerable progress in curing the bad habit of tension.

Chapter Seven

How to Keep from Hurrying
Yourself to Death

One of the most malicious causes of tension is our American habit of hurry. Learn to conquer hurry and you will have gone a long way toward bringing rhythmic relaxation into your activities. In fact, I will go so far as to say that if you will completely banish hurry you *will* be rhythmically relaxed.

For what are you really doing when you hurry? Are you not whipping yourself mentally, pouring on the pressure, coercing yourself into making greater and greater efforts—to do more and do it faster? If you stop hurrying, you need not necessarily accomplish less; you are just being more realistic. There is only so much that each of us can accomplish in a certain period of time, when we are functioning at the peak of our ability. If we put more pressure on ourselves to do more than this, we may get more done one time, or even a few times, but in the end the result is that we do less. A train engine that has an absolute top speed of 100 miles an hour will not go 150 miles an hour, merely because additional steam pressure is built up. What may very well happen is that the boiler will blow up or the train will jump the tracks.

Dr. Anthony Sidoni, Jr., Chief of Metabolics, Philadelphia General Hospital, has said that maturity is that state of being and thinking in which time has ceased to be all-demanding. Dr. Sidoni believes that if we leave some things to be done tomorrow, our chances of living to do them will increase materially.

Many people have the habit of hurry without realizing it. Learn to recognize hurry in your own life, and make a resolve to drop it. Hurry is not necessarily characterized by the speed with which you move or do things. Hurry is your subjective attitude. You can hurry while sitting down, apparently doing nothing. You can hurry while waiting for a bus. You can even hurry while lying in bed at night when you should be relaxing. It does no good to walk slowly if you are going to be running mentally.

Hurry not only makes you tense, and upsets your physical mechanism, but most of the time it does not even accomplish its alleged purpose—it doesn't always get the job done faster, but often actually slows you up.

You can learn to move with lightning speed without hurrying. And if you begin to hurry, you will find you cannot move so fast. In some recent experiments, students who had been trained to recognize minute muscular tensions were asked to make themselves hurry and to report what they experienced. They reported that, much to their surprise, they felt contractions in the opposing muscles. A student who was asked to report what happened to his leg muscles when he walked hurriedly said that when he extended his leg forward, using the muscles in the front of the leg, he felt contractions in the back of the leg at the same time, literally putting on the brakes, or holding him back.

Gil Dodds, the famous "miler," and holder of many world's records, has said that one of the reasons he was successful was that he never hurried, never pushed himself. Dodds wrote an article for *Guideposts* magazine in which he said that since it was well known that he said a prayer before each race, many people wanted to know what it was he prayed for. Dodds said that he never prayed for victory, or to beat anybody, or to run any faster than he could. Instead, he prayed that he would run the best race that was in him, that he would not be tempted to hurry in an attempt to beat some other runner.

Dodds claimed that he had his own pace or rhythm, and that he ran best when he maintained it. Hurry, pressure, and the attempt to make himself run faster than he could, broke his rhythm, and caused him to run slower. He told of one important race in which he was ahead but could not resist the temptation to hurry. The result was that he broke his rhythm, lost his stride, and saw the other runner pass him.

The refusal to hurry did not interfere with Dodds' determination to run as fast as he could, nor to get as much out of his physical machine as was possible. But when he was running as fast as he could, he did not feel that he ought to be running faster. He was content to do his best and not worry about whether that was good enough. This realistic attitude enabled Dodds to win many world's records on the track.

The great runner, Paavo Nurmi, always carried a watch with him in his races. He referred to his watch, not to the other runners. He insisted on running his own race, keeping his own tempo, regardless of the competition. He was another great champion who never hurried.

Albert Tangora was, for many years, the world's champion typist. In an article in *Opportunity* magazine called "Hurry Holds You Back," John D. Murphy told how Tangora increased his speed by slow-down practice. Tangora said that every time he reached a plateau of typing speed where he seemed to be stalled, he would practice for two weeks typing at about half his best speed. At the end of these two weeks of slow-down practice, he let himself out again, and always found that his speed had increased.

Instead of pressing, hurrying, and trying to force speed, Tangora did just the opposite. He forced himself to practice typing slowly. This slow practice—numerous repetitions performed without effort, hurry or strain— enabled his subconscious to learn typing better. Another way of expressing it would be to say that he perfected the link between mental imagery and muscular doing.

Effort and strain always inhibit learning. Relaxation aids learning.

Tangora had such remarkable success with this slow-down practice in typing that he tried it in shaving, dressing, and other everyday tasks. After two weeks of deliberately shaving slowly, he found that his shaving time was reduced by almost half when he once again let himself out. When you are tempted to hurry—or if you get a feeling of pressure when you perform some job— try this slow-down practice. Try slow-down practice in *all* your activities. There is no better technique for learning rhythmic relaxation.

Everyone has his own best pace or tempo for doing things. When we give in to hurry we allow external things and situations to set our pace for us. This is always a mistake, whether in the field of sports or the game of life. Set your own pace; play your own game.

How to Get Things Done

Although it seems rather obvious, many of us need to be told to remember that there is such a thing as time, and that anything we do in a space of time must be done one moment at a time, one step at a time. We cannot do all the steps instantaneously, any more than we can play a whole musical composition by striking all the notes in it at once.

A housewife recently said to me: "When I start to do my housework and think of all the work I have to do,

I just start churning inside." Without quite realizing it, she was trying to get it all done at once, which was her secret desire. Tension from impatience is nearly always due to an unconscious unwillingness to go through with the job in an orderly way.

Remember the story of the gladiator who faced three opponents in the arena? He turned and ran around and around the circular enclosure until his three opponents were widely separated. Then he turned on his nearest pursuer and slew him. He ran to meet the next pursuer and slew him. Then there was only one opponent left, and he defeated him easily.

This is the best technique we can use in defeating our own enemies, tension and hurry. It requires a minimum of effort and no strain or pressure at all to wash one dish calmly, sign one letter, take one step. It requires no strain or effort to live life minute by minute. And with all our straining and hurrying, that is the only way we can live it. As a physical organism you can function only in the present moment. You cannot function in the future or in the past. But trying to do so can make you tense and irritable. Plan for the future. Learn from the past. But if you want to function properly, reduce your area of trying to the present moment.

When you are thinking about your work, break it up into small parts and cope with each part one by one. Writing this book could easily have become a tension-making situation. But I made up my mind that I was not writing a book. I will never write a book. I shall write only one page. When that is finished, I shall write another.

There is no job or task that this principle cannot be applied to. If you have a sink full of dishes to wash, say to yourself: "I am going to wash just one dish. I know I can wash one dish without any effort or strain," and proceed to wash that one dish as if it were all in the world you had to do. It is all in the world you have to do at that moment. You couldn't wash the other dishes in the sink even if you tried.

If you are an executive signing your mail, say to yourself: "I am going to sign my name to just one letter." I have noticed that many men grip the pen and tighten up their jaw muscles as if they were faced with a job requiring tremendous muscular effort. One man had become so habitually tense that he even tensed up when trying to sign just one letter. Let us say his name was John Doe. "If all you had to do was to make a 'J,' do you think you could do it without any sense of strain?" I asked him. I then asked him to write a "J" for me. As soon as he had finished, I asked him to make an "o," and so on until he had written his full name, "John Doe." In a short while he was signing his name automatically again. He not only signed many letters in the course of a day with no sense of effort, strain or hurry, but he told me that he found he was able to sign his mail in about twenty-five per cent less time.

I have told typists who seemed to tense up automatically whenever they began to type a letter: "Say to your-

self, 'I am going to put a piece of paper in the typewriter.'
Think only of getting the paper in the machine. Then
say to yourself, 'I am going to type in the date,' and proceed to do it without any sense of hurry, effort, or strain.
Then say to yourself, 'Now I am going to type in the
name and address,' and proceed through the whole letter in this fashion." I have recommended that some typists break down the job even further and have for their
goal, or area of effort, the striking of but one key, and
then to set up another area of effort which includes the
striking of only one more key.

If any bosses who are reading this think I am sug-
gesting that their typists should do less work, let me
point out that this method has been tried and has increased production as much as twenty-five per cent. Not
only will your typist get out more letters in the course of
a day, but she'll feel better, will be easier to get along
with, and won't miss as much time from work recover-
ing from eyestrain and sick headache. And remember,
it was by a slow-down technique that Albert Tangora became the world's champion typist.

Life is not a hundred-yard dash, but more in the
nature of a cross-country run. If we sprint all the time,
we not only fail to win the race, but we never even last
long enough to reach the finish line.

The principle of reducing the area of effort enables you to get things done that you would ordinarily
never begin at all. Why is it that most of us are inclined
to put off writing a letter, cleaning out the attic, visiting

the dentist, and a hundred and one other jobs that we intend to do some day but just never get around to? In large measure it is because our anticipated area of effort is so big it scares us off. It defeats our will to work.

Limit your area of effort on the jobs you want to get done. Don't say: "Some day I am going to clean out that old attic." Instead, say, and mean it: "I have a little time, and I think I will take a few things out of the attic." If all you intend to do is to "take a few things out of the attic," you'll find that you have the necessary will and appetite for it. It may well happen that once you get started and get warmed up you'll extend your area of effort because you want to, and end up by cleaning the whole attic, but don't count on it. Be content to accomplish only the small part of the task you have set for yourself at that particular time. In fact, it is better if you quit the job while you still have an appetite for it, and before you get fed up.

The will to work has a tendency to grow and spread all by itself when you indulge it and exercise it. It does not grow by your trying to force it.

A prominent writer once found that she had lost her will to write. She no longer had any stomach for the job. What had been fun became a dreaded task. For a time she tried to force herself to write a certain number of hours a day—and she grew steadily worse. Finally, she decided she would write only one page, and that she wouldn't care whether what she wrote was good or bad. Every day she sat down and wrote something. Soon she found her one page extending into two, then three, then four. In a few months she was producing more than ever and selling it.

Someone has said that "life is just one darned thing after another." This bit of philosophy should help us realize that when we get our present job done, our doing will not be over and done with forever. There will be something else to do tomorrow. There is no use resenting the fact. That is what life is. Many of us look forward unconsciously to some future time when there will be nothing to do—when we get off from work, when we get the house painted, when we get the children educated, when we have a certain amount of money in the bank. But life itself is movement, action, and doing. As long as we are alive there will be things we will have to do to keep alive.

Give Yourself Plenty of Time

Many people feel hurried because they think there just isn't enough time. Sir William Osler, in one of his talks to students, told them to think of how much time there is for you to use, rather than of how little time there is.

The first hour in the day nearly always sets the tempo for the entire day. If you start the day a little behind time it is very likely that you will never catch up all day. Much of the sense of hurry and pressure could be eliminated by the simple expedient of getting up fifteen minutes or half an hour earlier in the morning. This extra half hour will help to make the whole day calm and unhurried, and will do your nerves much more good than the additional sleep would. Anything you might gain from the extra sleep will be offset by the sense of pressure you will have all day because you started the day in a hurried, tense way. Go through the day a few minutes late and your nerves are on edge all day; go through the day a few minutes ahead of time, and you can relax.

Most of us have been taught from our youth that we must make every minute count. Trying to crowd three days' activities into one hectic day is not making the most of time. Time that we do not use to our best advantage is time wasted, regardless of the number of motions that we may go through.

It is also well to remember that clocks were made by man for his own convenience, in order to make time serve man better. Today, many of us have reversed the process, and have become slaves to the clock.

When you have an appointment, don't wait until the last moment to get started. If you're delayed in traffic, you'll be so tense and nervous when you arrive that you'll undoubtedly make a mess of things. It doesn't help you to make a good impression on the other fellow if you have to start out with an apology for being late. This puts you at an immediate disadvantage. If you have left yourself plenty of time to get there, you will be calm and ready to tackle the business at hand when you arrive. If you arrive a few minutes early you will have a chance to marshal your thoughts, and you will also put the other person in the position of having to apologize for having kept you waiting!

Give Yourself Time to Think

Chronic hurriers usually believe that unless they are actively engaged in pushing, striving, thinking and working every moment, they are wasting time. Newton was not wasting time when he was sitting under that apple tree!

The French scientist, Fehr, once said that fully ninety per cent of the creative ideas came to scientists in idle moments when they were away from their work. These creative ideas never come when you are feeling harassed, hurried, or tense.

Most of us stay in such a state of hurry and tension that we never give our subconscious a chance to work for us. We go through life trying to solve all our problems and get all the answers with our puny little conscious intellect, when there is a giant in the background waiting to serve us. And here again, the way to make your subconscious work for you is to relax your muscles, and to learn to keep them relaxed except when they are needed for a specific task.

Men and women who are forever pushing themselves, forever hurrying themselves to an early grave, might ask themselves: "What is time to a dead man?" And make no mistake about it, hurry is a killer.

The American Heart Association has published an excellent little booklet, called *The Heart of the Home,* which can be purchased for ten cents. In it this useful advice is found: "The rate of speed at which you live is important. Hasty thinking and hasty working seldom accomplish what you want. . . . Find for yourself the rhythmic, relaxed way of doing things and you will accomplish more, have fewer accidents, and spend less energy."

Hurry, pressure, and tension are enemies of your work and your health. Banish them by relaxation, and you'll feel better, live longer and do better.

It will also help you to acquire the habit of relaxation if you will remember that tension is the handmaiden of hurry. Remove tension and it is impossible to hurry. While tension is more or less unconscious with the average person, the feeling of hurry is conscious and easily recognized. Hurry is like the needle indicator on the pressure gauge, which you can see, and which tells you about the pressure in the boiler, which you can't see.

Create a mental "slow" sign in your mind, and every time you feel a sense of hurry, deliberately slow down. Slow down not only your physical movements, but slow down on the desire to go faster than your most efficient pace. Be willing to take it slower. In other words, don't let your foot ride so heavily on your mental accelerator. Ultimately you'll go faster and get more done by increasing your natural tempo—not by forcing time.

Chapter Eight

Ways to Obtain Sound Sleep

A Gallup poll showed that fifty-two per cent of our population suffers, to some extent, from insomnia. Each year more than three billion sleeping pills are sold. Yet, except in truly pathological conditions, nothing could be easier than sleeping. It requires no doing at all; it is complete not doing.

Insomnia isn't something that happens to you. It requires doing on your part. We fail to go to sleep because, for one reason or another, in one way or another, we interfere with automatic processes by making efforts. The trouble is that we do not realize that we are interfering, or just how we are interfering. It is the purpose of this chapter to show you just how we do interfere with sleep by making efforts unconsciously. Only when you realize what it is you are doing that keeps you awake, will you be able to stop doing it.

You will also learn how you can begin sleep passively relaxed. Many people do not relax fully even in sleep. They wake up as tired as when they went to bed. Learn how to begin sleep in a completely relaxed way and you will sleep that way all night.

Your ability or inability to go to sleep quickly depends as much or more upon what you do and don't do during the day as it does upon what you do when you go to bed. You cannot work or play in a tense, anxious, frantic state all day and expect your body to relax all these accumulated tensions automatically the minute your head touches the pillow. If you carry accumulated tensions to bed with you, you must not expect sleep until the tensions have been relaxed away. Yet this is exactly what most people do expect.

When you do carry accumulated tensions to bed with you, you must be willing to relax them away patiently. There is no need to waste time scolding yourself because you allowed yourself to get tense. Begin to relax away your tensions quietly and methodically. Sleep will come when you prepare your body for it.

Many people who complain that they can't shed their worries and tensions when they get into bed really mean that they don't dare. They feel that they cannot afford to relax, even when they go to bed, because of world conditions, or because of some personal problem that remains unsolved. If you could settle world conditions by tensing your brow, or solve your personal problems by clenching your teeth, I would be the last to recommend that you stop doing these things. But you can't. On the other hand, you can't learn to drop your worries and cares when you go to bed by convincing yourself that you have a right to do so. You just make the decision to drop them—with no conditions.

Many people are proud of their insomnia. It is one of

the favorite topics of conversation whenever two or more people get together. We brag about our insomnia. What we are really saying when we tell someone, "I didn't sleep a wink last night" is "See how haggard and worn I am, see how concerned I am about the proper matters, see what a load I carry." If you will merely stop talking about your insomnia, you may be surprised to find that it has gone away simply because you are no longer using it to satisfy your ego.

Many people punish themselves with insomnia. If you have made a mistake—even a grievous one—punishing yourself with insomnia will not erase it. If you have made such a mistake, you will need physical energy and a clear head if you are going to try to correct it the next day. Sleep and relaxation can help you repair the damage; insomnia can't. If you made a mistake during the day, be man or woman enough to accept the fact that you made a mistake. Don't try to erase it or cover it up by self-punishment. If you admit the mistake to yourself, you will go to sleep. Must everyone think you are perfect? Are you too good ever to make a mistake? Accept the fact that you may be less than perfect. Using insomnia as self-punishment comes from the egotistic desire to regard ourselves as perfect, as incapable of making mistakes. The unconscious reasons something like this: "I made a mistake. But I cannot accept this fact. I cannot admit it to myself or to others. I learned in childhood that punishment erases a mistake and makes everything all right again. I will punish myself, erase the mistake, and save myself from the painful experience of having to acknowledge myself as less than perfect."

I have found that the athlete who pulls a boner and tries to convince the coach and himself that he is sorry, or that it wasn't his fault, is much more likely to make another costly mistake, than the boy who accepts his mistake without undue self-recrimination, and studies it objectively to see what he did wrong so that he can avoid making the same mistake a second time. In the first instance, the focus is on the self. The boy who suffers from the mistake is concerned primarily with his own ego; the boy who learns from the mistake is concerned primarily with the situation and the ways of correcting it.

Banish the Fear of Insomnia

Not everyone who has insomnia is kept awake by worries and problems. Every insomniac is not trying to punish himself. There are many other things that can cause insomnia. But, there is one common denominator in all insomnia; there is one factor that is always present. This big factor is fear of not being able to go to sleep. When you overcome fear of insomnia, you go to sleep. This brings us back to relaxation, for relaxation banishes fear. When you let your muscles go, you let your fears go.

It will also help you banish the fear of insomnia if you understand that no one ever loses the ability to sleep. When I was Physical-Training Director at Bill Brown's

Health Farm, I met many executives who claimed to have lost the ability to sleep naturally. One man claimed he had not had a night's sleep, without some sort of medication, for the past twenty years! Yet this same man was sleeping more soundly and more restfully than he had in twenty years, after one week of studying how to get natural sleep through relaxation.

Your body no more forgets how to sleep than your heart forgets how to beat, or your lungs how to breathe. You can upset any bodily function by consciously doing things that interfere with it. But you do not have to do anything drastic to bring it back to normal. All that you have to do is to stop interfering, and to let your body do its own work. When you stop being tense, your body adjusts itself automatically to its natural rhythm.

Numerous tests have shown that prolonged insomnia does no permanent damage to your physical machine. It may damage the performance of the machine as long as you suffer from it, but it doesn't hurt the machine itself. Low octane gasoline does not damage your automobile motor. All it does is reduce its efficiency. Start using high-octane gas and your motor performs as well as ever. An occasional bad night does not even reduce your operating efficiency the next day very much. You can think just as fast, or perhaps faster, and you can do almost as much physical work, except that you will expend more effort in your thinking and your working.

It does not really matter whether you go to sleep

quickly, or whether you sleep soundly, on any particular night. Loss of an entire night's sleep does no irreparable damage to your body or brain. Experiments with college students have shown that the human body can go without any sleep at all for as long as 72 hours, with no physiological damage. These experiments also showed that it requires a great deal of trouble and ingenuity on the part of the experimenter to keep even nervous, light sleepers awake this long. Long before insomnia can damage your body, nature will step in and put you to sleep.

On the "Truth or Consequences" radio and TV show, Ralph Edwards once offered a contestant five thousand dollars if he would be asleep at two P.M. on a certain day in the pressroom of a large newspaper. The contestant had one week to prepare for this test; during that week he could lose as much sleep as he pleased, or do anything he liked to tire himself. But at the appointed time he was examined by a doctor and was found to be awake. Edwards did not run much of a risk. Offering someone a large reward to go to sleep is about the best way to guarantee that he will remain awake. The promise of the reward creates an ideal condition for insomnia. The contestant becomes anxious to go to sleep, he begins unconsciously to make efforts to go to sleep, and the more he tries to go to sleep, the more wakeful he becomes.

Many insomniacs have made a good night's sleep in itself such a desired goal that they place themselves unwittingly in the same situation as Ralph Edwards' contestant. A good night's sleep becomes for them the equivalent of the five-thousand-dollar prize. Such people need to learn to relax somewhat their frantic, fretful desire for sleep.

Of course, sleep is precious. We need it. Good, sound, restful sleep enables us to start the day off rested and relaxed. It enables us to do our work without so much expenditure of effort. But there is no need to grow tense and anxious about sleep merely because it is precious and necessary. Breathing is also necessary, but we don't worry about that. Sleep is as natural and easy as breathing, and we should think of it in the same way. Not only is it easy and natural to sleep, but you would find it a difficult job indeed to keep yourself awake over any extended period of time. The insomniac who says, "I didn't sleep a wink last night," thinks he is telling the truth. But he probably slept a great deal more than he supposes.

Also, be suspicious of the person who tells you he is all worn out because he couldn't go to sleep the night before. The chances are that it was not the loss of sleep itself that wore him out, but that he wore himself out fretting, twisting and squirming. If he had remained quiet and calm, had relaxed his muscles, he would have obtained the equivalent of 80 to 90 per cent of a good night's sleep—even if he had remained awake all night. And, if he had done this, he would have gone to sleep in spite of himself.

How to Woo Sleep

There are certain things we can do to bring sleep. But before we can make them work, we must give up the idea that we can will ourselves to sleep by trying. Acknowledging that sleep is beyond our direct conscious control enables us to stop trying, and puts us in the right frame of mind to learn how we can bring sleep, not directly and volitionally, but indirectly, by preparing the ground for it.

Sleep comes when the body is more or less relaxed and the mind is not being stimulated by impressions from the five sense organs. Quiet and dark aid sleep, because such conditions cut out stimulations to the mind from the eyes and ears. On the other hand, a continuous monotonous noise—rain on the roof, the chirping of crickets, the drone of a motor, a dull sermon—puts us to sleep. So does continuous staring down a straight highway. The reason for this is that the mind refuses to allow itself to be bored. When the scenery or the sound gets monotonous and dull, the eye may continue to see and the ear to hear, but the mind just doesn't bother to look at or listen to their incoming signals any more. A speaker in the House of Commons once upbraided Winston Churchill with: "Mr. Churchill, how can you form an opinion of what I am saying if you are asleep?" To which Churchill answered, "Sleep *is* an opinion."

While our evenings need not be dull in order for us

to sleep, the hours just preceding sleep should not be too stimulating. It is better to spend the last hour before bedtime in quiet contemplation of the day's activities, in quiet conversation, or in some other form of activity that is not too mentally stimulating. Just as you need a period of warming up to start the day, you need some period of tapering off to end it. Even fifteen minutes will serve, once you get the knack of it. No matter how late it is, you will sleep better if you spend a few minutes setting the stage for sleep. You are about to enter into a completely different mental and physical environment from the one you have been in all day. Do not plunge in suddenly. Set the stage for sleep. This might be called, getting in the mood for sleep.

Spend five minutes relaxing in an easy chair. If possible, have someone read you the formula. If you have an open fireplace, gaze lazily into the fire. If you haven't one, look in memory and imagination at some relaxing scene from the past. Remember some time in your life when you were so sleepy and drowsy you just couldn't keep your eyes open. Yawn and stretch. Become conscious of how tired you are. Allow yourself to visualize the cool, inviting, clean, white sheets on your bed, and the soft pillow waiting for your head. Think of how restful and refreshing it is going to be to snuggle in to bed.

In other words, spend a short time contemplating sleep. When you do this you are using step three of the formula—using mental imagery. Don't make a chore or duty of your tapering off period. Keep it simple, and easy, and natural.

If you suffer from eyestrain, or if you have a tendency to keep thinking after you are in bed, try performing, easily and lazily, just before bed, a hundred of the swings described on page 57. They will relax your eyes and reduce mental visual activity.

Try to form the habit of going to bed at approximately the same time each night. This, after a certain length of time, tends to set up a sleep rhythm in your twenty-four hours—so that you automatically begin to grow somewhat sleepy when this regular bedtime grows near.

And So to Bed

You are now in bed, and in a mood to let yourself go to sleep. In times past you have chosen this time to indulge in worry pictures, to twist and turn, and to fret because you cannot make yourself go to sleep.

We are going to change all that quite easily and simply by giving you something else to do. You cannot attend to two things at once. Before, you had no positive goal toward which to direct your attention, and so your attention got mixed up with negatives—or the things you didn't want to happen. Or, if you did have a positive goal for your attention, it was just the vague general one of making yourself go to sleep. You have found that this, too, keeps you awake.

Now you are not going to try to put yourself to

sleep. You are not even particularly concerned with sleep one way or the other. You are going to be concerned only with the performance of certain definite acts.

First, you are going to begin to breathe consciously in the sleep rhythm, by consciously paying attention to your incoming and outgoing breaths. Natural sleep breathing is done with the diaphragm, not the chest. Lie on your back and breathe with your abdomen. Let your abdomen rise as you breathe in and fall as you breathe out. Your chest should rise and fall very slightly, if at all. Breathe in slowly through your nose—not in the front part of your nose, but way back where the nasal chambers join the throat—in the nasopharynx. It may not be scientifically correct to say that one can breathe in at the front part of the nose, or at the back of the nasal chambers, but if you will experiment a little—remembering how a sleeping person's breathing sounds—you will soon find that by breathing in a certain way, you get the sensation that your breathing is far back in your head. The sound of the breath coming in will not be a sniff at the end of your nose, but will come from your throat and will sound something like a basketball bladder being inflated.

After you have breathed in slowly, retain your breath for just a fraction of a second, and then let the air out by relaxing the diaphragm. Don't force the air out with a grunt, and don't let it out slowly by holding it back. Just let go, and let it come out of its own accord, just as if it were coming from a punctured balloon.

Diaphragmatic, or belly breathing, relaxes muscular tensions in the abdominal area and helps keep your internal organs from becoming spastic. It also has a reflex action on your whole body. After you get the knack of it, you can feel tensions draining out of your entire body, with each outgoing, relaxed breath.

Next, you are going to go over your entire body quickly and let go any tensions you detect—while continuing the belly breathing. When you are working alone, as most readers will be doing when going to sleep at night, it is not wise to spend a lot of time consciously relaxing each part of the body. This has all the aspects of a big job, or a chore, and if you undertake it in that way you will unconsciously make excess efforts.

It is usually better to concentrate on relaxing only the forehead, eyes, and jaw, after a quick look at the rest of your body to see that you are not holding your legs, arms, and trunk excessively tense.

Relaxing the forehead, eyes, and jaw does not seem to be such a big job. You need not get tense thinking about it. And when these areas are perfectly relaxed, sleep comes. These are the areas that are associated with seeing, thinking, talking, and doing. Relaxing them automatically relaxes the seeing, thinking, talking, and doing areas of the mind.

Begin with your forehead. Frown and pay attention to the tension that is present. Then tell yourself mentally to let the tension go. It is not necessary to try to give yourself auto-suggestions such as: "Now my forehead is very relaxed." Just talk to yourself mentally: "Now I am making my forehead tense, now I will let it go a little, now a little more," etc.

This vocalizing of instructions helps in the early stages of learning any skill. Notice a man on a job learning to operate a new machine. Notice how he instructs himself: "Now I pull this knob out here. Next I turn this wheel to the left," etc. This vocalizing keeps his attention focused on what he is doing, allows him to see exactly what it is he is doing, and thus enables him to do it without strain. The pilots on commercial airlines vocalize each thing they do on the take-off and landing. So do many surgeons when performing a delicate operation.

Next proceed to your eyes, and then to your jaw— giving yourself the instructions as they appear in the formula, just as if you were giving them to another person. As you give each instruction, obey it automatically, without thinking about it, without any fuss or bother.

When you have finished relaxing your jaw, remember the black dots we talked about before. Remember the large black dot at the top of the diagram on page 62. Then shift your attention to the small black dot at the bottom. Then shift your attention back to the large dot at the top. Do not try to see them—just remember how they looked. Shift your mental vision back and forth from top to bottom. As you do so, you will probably see the dots jump in the opposite direction. As you shift up, the dots will seem to shift down; as you shift down, they will seem to shift up. As a variation, make up your own diagrams to remember. Try remembering how the numerals from 1 to 9 look. Remember the letters of the lower-case alphabet from "a" to "z." Imagine a simple dumbbell consisting of two small black dots joined together by a thin, black line.

A friend of mine tells me that he puts himself to sleep by visualizing one of the numerals from 1 to 10. He picks out one numeral and visualizes it as it would look if drawn upon a large white square with a black frame around it. Experiment until you find the simple diagram that is easiest for you to remember.

Do not attempt to see these diagrams with your eyes, nor to imagine them before your eyes as you lie in bed. Do not try to make them appear in space before your closed eyelids. Some students find it easier to remember the diagrams if they start off by imagining that they are entering the living room where this book stands on a bookshelf. In imagination, they go across the living room, take the book from the shelf, go to the sofa, seat themselves comfortably, and open the book to the page showing the black dots.

These are all only suggestions of things you can do, but remember that you do not have to do any of these things in order to go to sleep. If you find yourself straining, or making efforts, when going through any one part of this sleep routine, drop it, at least temporarily, and do only those parts that come easily. Don't make the sleep routine unpleasant, or a duty, or a chore. Its very essence is pleasantness, ease, and absence of strain.

When All Else Fails

Some people, without meaning to, unconsciously make an effort not to make an effort, when they are doing something that calls for not trying. If this should happen to you, and you find yourself tense or restless after trying the sleep routine, don't worry about it. There is still something else you can do about going to sleep.

Since making an effort to go to sleep is keeping you awake, and you seem bound and determined to make some sort of effort anyhow, simply stop making an effort to go to sleep and consciously make a deliberate effort to remain awake. Do deliberately whatever it is you are doing that is keeping you awake.

If you genuinely give up the desire to go to sleep for the time being, and desire instead to make yourself tense and wakeful, you will relieve yourself of all anxiety about sleep. Also, as you become proficient, through practice, in doing consciously and on purpose those things that have been keeping you awake (and that you have been performing unconsciously heretofore, without your will or volition), you acquire conscious control over them. Conscious control gives you the power to do or not do them, as you choose.

When you find that your breathing is nervous and fast, in spite of your attempts to relax, then deliberately practice breathing in just this way. Keep up the nervous, fast breathing for a hundred breaths. And, if necessary, take an additional hundred.

If there is a tight feeling in your chest, try to reproduce it consciously and voluntarily. See if you can make it worse. If you can, it means you are acquiring some slight ability to control it. Practice will enable you to control it still more.

If there are butterflies in your stomach, try to analyze the feeling exactly, and see if you can produce it at will.

If your jaws insist on tensing up, after you have tried to relax them, practice clenching them deliberately a hundred times.

If worrying thoughts insist on running round and round in your mind, without your conscious permission, deliberately make them run faster and see if you can worry even more for at least fifteen minutes.

There is no catch to this method. If you actually begin to try hard to do those things that keep you awake, several nights' practice will not only give you some degree of skill in consciously controlling them, but you will, automatically, by directing your efforts to wakefulness, abandon all efforts to go to sleep. Make an excess effort to stay awake, and you fail to do it, just as making an excess effort to go to sleep keeps you awake!

By using either the sleep routine, or negative practice, or both, you can learn to acquire good sleeping habits in a comparatively short time. Notice that neither method requires that you try to put yourself to sleep.

The Proper Attitude

When I tell some people they should never do anything to try to go to sleep, they say: "You say I am to make no effort to go to sleep—to do absolutely nothing to go to sleep—and yet you give me these instructions about how to relax when I get in bed—visualizing a black dot, watching my breathing, relaxing my forehead —isn't this doing something to try to go to sleep?"

My answer is a question: "Before you go to bed there are certain things that you do already. You take off your clothes. Perhaps you take a bath. You brush your teeth. Lastly, you walk to your bed, turn out the light, and crawl underneath the covers. You do all these things. Do you do them to put yourself to sleep?"

"No, certainly not."

"Then why do you do these things?"

"I undress, turn out the light, and get into bed—not with the idea that these things will put me to sleep. I do them in preparation for sleep."

"Then do your relaxation practice, and your visualizing, for exactly the same reason. Turn off your tension switches in the same way that you turn off your light; untie your muscles in the same way that you untie your shoes. Do not try to relax to put yourself to sleep. Undress your body of tensions, in the same way that you undress it of clothes."

Chapter Nine

Relax and Win

The secret of maintaining rhythmic relaxation during stiff competition, or when working or playing in other pressure situations, lies in a simple trick of selecting your mental images. Concern yourself with, or mentally consider, the outcome and you become tense. You make it impossible to play with rhythmic relaxation, and at the peak of your performance. Take your mental eyes off the scoreboard, and concern yourself with the immediate job at hand, and you will find it possible to maintain rhythmic relaxation. This, in turn, will enable you to make the best score possible for you.

"When once a decision is reached, and execution is the order of the day, dismiss absolutely all responsibility and care about the outcome. Unclamp, in a word, your intellectual and practical machinery, and let it run free; and the service it will do you will be twice as good . . . . Such a habit, like other habits, can be formed." *

Over-concern with final results makes us tense because it makes us put forth excess efforts. There is nothing that we can do about the final score with our

* *On Vital Reserves,* by William James. Henry Holt & Co., New York.

muscles, except to do our best with the job we have to do at the moment. If we do this, we will be making a specific effort to do the one thing at hand, and will then be working and playing with rhythmic relaxation.

Over-concern with final results is the same thing as fear of failure. Fear of failure is a negative image in the mind. Our muscles continue to try to obey our mental images. Therefore, it is impossible for you to let yourself out and plunge into a job wholeheartedly when you fear failure. You are literally trying to do and not do at the same time. You are going forward with your brakes on.

Every football season some highly favored unbeaten team will suddenly get upset by a team that has no record to uphold, has nothing to lose, and goes on the field relaxed. Even so, it isn't really the underdog team that defeats the favorite; it is the favored team's own negative images. The members of the unbeaten team are under pressure to keep up their record; they are concerned with what they don't want to happen in the end, rather than with what they have to do at the moment.

Hugh Casey, one of the greatest relief pitchers of all time, did most of his pitching in pressure situations. When the atmosphere got so tense you could almost slice it, they called in "the Old Fireman," to put out the fire. Casey was asked once why he walked from the bull pen to the pitcher's mound so slowly, and with his head down. "When I'm walking with my head down," he said, "I am thinking. I am going over in my mind just exactly what it is I want to do. I make up my mind I am going to make the batter hit where I want him to." Casey was concerning himself with what *he* wanted to happen.

The pitcher who gets rattled and loses all control is concerned with what the batter might do to him. He concerns himself with what he doesn't want to happen. Many a pitcher can pitch air-tight baseball until something happens to put the pressure on—the infield makes an error, and a runner goes to third base; a long-ball hitter comes to bat. In these situations the pitcher changes his focus and mentally looks at a negative image. He puts forth extra special effort to get himself out of a jam. The effort destroys his groove, or rhythmic relaxation.

Forming the habit of positive rather than negative imagery is not a mystical or magical process. It merely requires that you keep the focus of your attention upon your doing in the present, rather than upon what might happen in the future.

If I hold up the index fingers of my right and left hands three feet apart, you can choose the finger you want to focus your eyes on You can focus on my right index finger, even if you are tempted to think you ought to look at the left one. Focusing your mental look on the present job and on the positive thing you want to do is just as simple. The only difficulty is that you have looked upon the negative for so long that you tend to do it unconsciously unless you stop and think. In order to form the habit of positive imagery you must practice consciously directing your mental look to the positive. After sufficient practice, this, too, will become habitual.

Jerry Travers was one of the greatest golf competitors that ever lived. He won the U. S. Amateur four times, and the Open once. Travers used to say that there is only one important shot in golf and that is the next shot. He said he never thought about a shot he had played poorly, or missed, because it was gone and could not be played again.

During a pennant race when Leo Durocher was managing the New York Giants he was asked if he thought they could win it. "We are thinking only of to-day's game," he said. "We have kept this thing on a day-to-day basis and that is the way we are going to play it out." Durocher's advice to his players, to keep them relaxed, was "Keep your eyes off the scoreboard and your eye on the ball."

Winning Is None of Your Business

Know what it is you wish to do. Form a clear mental picture of your goal. But don't try to "do" the end result. Relax and let your mind and muscles fulfill your mental images by doing effectively the job at hand.

Ironically enough, you stand a better chance of winning if winning in itself is not all-important to you. To try to "win" is a weak, generalized effort. To play the next shot, or to keep your eye on the ball, is a specific effort. If you become too much concerned with the scoreboard, you detract from your concentration and your efficiency in doing the job at hand—the specific task that can lead to victory.

A professional automobile racer came to me for advice. As he expressed it, his nerves were shot, and he was losing his grip, as well as losing too many races.

"You are mainly concerned with winning, aren't you?" I asked him.

"Of course," he said, "that's my business."

"No, it isn't," I told him. "Your business is to get everything out of your car that you possibly can, and to be alert enough to take advantage of every break. You cannot do this if all your attention is focused on winning."

"I think I see your point," he said. Soon he was back in his old form—and winning races again.

In our society, we tend to overemphasize the importance of winning, regardless of cost. You do not need to be the best, or the most, or the first, in order to have a successful, satisfying life. There are thousands of good lawyers, doctors, engineers, businessmen, and farmers in this country who are leading successful lives despite the fact that they are neither the best nor the first in their fields. Does their accomplishment become less because somewhere in the world someone has accomplished more?

The mistaken idea that we have a moral obligation to be the first and the best is one of the big causes of tension in our society. It is impossible for a man to relax if he feels that he is disgraced before God and man if he does not live in the biggest house in his neighborhood, drive the biggest car, have the biggest bankroll. Many a man runs himself to death trying to keep up with the Joneses, and has no energy left for his own accomplishment.

Joe Louis had about as relaxed an attitude about winning as any competitor I have ever seen. He was noted for his dead-pan expression, for the calm, unhurried, nerveless and deliberate way he went about his business. He never got too tense or excited over a fight because he said that he knew if he was better than the other fighter, and didn't make too many mistakes, he would win. If he wasn't better, he didn't think he deserved to win. After the first Conn fight, during which Louis had tried in vain to find an opening up to the thirteenth round, a reporter asked Louis if he had gotten discouraged, or feared that he was losing the fight. "No," he said, "I couldn't get to him, but there was nothing I could do about it. I was willing to wait. I didn't know whether he would open up or not, but I knew if he did I would get him; if he didn't, I wouldn't." He waited patiently and when Conn did open up, at last, Louis was able to take advantage of the brief opportunity and get to him. Had his brain and muscles been frozen with tension and anxiety, he would never have been able to move with the lightning speed and perfect timing that won the fight for him.

Don't Make Winning a Moral Issue

In a sense, every competitor should have a healthy and realistic desire to win. If nobody wanted to win, there would be no point in having races. We need incentives and rewards. We need to want rewards.

Incentives call forth and arouse powers within us that we never dreamed we possessed. A challenge should call forth, and make us aware of, powers that would otherwise remain dormant. That, as I see it, is the main value of athletics. The competition, the challenge, the incentive, should teach us that we have reserves of power that can be called upon when a demand is made for them. A realistic incentive also serves to arouse and develop the will to win, which is far different from neurotic anxiety about results.

A healthy incentive, and a healthy desire to win, give us the innate satisfaction of creative doing. We get pleasure from the action itself, from calling upon and using our dormant powers, from the thrill of risk and adventure, from pitting our resources against obstacles and overcoming them. But the neurotic desire to win has none of this. The only satisfaction we get in this case is the ego-satisfaction of beating someone else, if we succeed in winning. Would you obtain any genuine satisfaction from winning a foot race with your eight-year-old son? If the mere act of winning is all-important, you should obtain a real satisfaction from bettering him.

Would you obtain any real satisfaction, or do anything to develop your own powers, if you knocked out a boxer who had one hand handcuffed to his belt?

Behind this neurotic desire to win is the fear of losing or coming in second best. Winning in itself has no value. But we have given it a value. When we become ashamed to lose after we have given our best, when we feel guilty and disgraced after our best has not been good enough, the desire to win has become neurotic. It is not the fear of losing a loving cup, a pennant on the end of a stick, or even a million dollars, that makes a person become tensely over-concerned with results. It is the threat to his ego, the feeling that he will be shown up as an inferior person. Are you less than what you are, because someone else is more? Does the dime in my pocket become less than a dime because I know that someone else has a dollar? Does my home become less comfortable to live in, because I learn that someone else has a mansion?

Our big mistake is that we have made a moral issue out of the mere act of winning: to win is right; to lose is wrong; to win is to be a hero; to lose is to be personally disgraced.

In my work with young boys I have found that in many cases an over-concern to be the best keeps a boy from competing at all. He is afraid to take a chance on losing because of the personal disgrace involved. If he does get into a contest, he makes only a token effort, and cannot go all out, because then if he loses he can always save face by pointing out that after all he wasn't really trying.

This is what I tell athletes who suffer from this personality disease: "Don't ever be afraid to be caught trying—and trying your very best. If you fall flat on your face get up and plunge in, and fall flat on your face again if necessary."

Relax—and Let Your Subconscious Do It

In training basketball players, I sometimes tell a boy: "Do not waste time wondering where the ball is going, or whether or not you are going to shoot a goal. Just get a mental image clearly in your mind of the ball going through the basket, relax all care of responsibility about results, and throw it."

I do not tell him that this is some magical process that will make the ball go through the basket every time. He would find out soon enough that I was wrong and would then lose faith in the method. Instead, I tell him: "If you miss, your mind will subconsciously note the degree of error and will make the appropriate correction next time, if you don't interfere with the process."

Not long ago, a friend asked me if relaxation could improve his golf game. He had trouble with his putting especially. I told him to look over the green, notice the contour, make a mental note of the distance from ball to cup, form a mental picture of the ball dropping into the cup, and then just step up and hit away without being too careful about it. After two weeks of this relaxed practice he broke 90 for the first time in his life.

Ben Hogan always makes a shot mentally before actually making it. He makes a perfect shot in his mind, then steps up and lets his muscles carry out his mental images. Hogan calls this "muscle memory," and says that his muscles remember what to do in order to make a good shot.

Some years ago, Johnny Bulla wrote an article for *Golfing* magazine in which he said that a clear mental image of the ball going just where you wanted it to go, and the calm assumption that it would go there, were more important than form. He mentioned many of golfdom's great players, and pointed out that all of them were guilty of errors in form that would bring anguish to any golf pro if he observed them in one of his students. But Bulla said that these errors in form were compensated for by the subconscious making some correction that would negate the errors. Bulla said that the most important thing was to hold the completed act as an image in the mind. The subconscious (the automatic-functioning level of the mind) would then, after sufficient practice, find a way to fulfill that image, in spite of errors in form.

Why do you suppose some golfers find it so much easier to hit the sand trap than to hit the green? A friend of mine never misses the trap on the seventh hole of his club's course, but he has never hit the green. Although he tries as hard as he can to miss it, the sand trap is the dominant image in his mind, and that is where his ball goes.

Have you ever considered that the average sand trap is much smaller than the green? The odds are much greater that your ball will hit the green than the trap. But golfers who couldn't hit the green to save their lives hit the sand trap with maddening regularity. What other explanation could there be except that the golfer's muscles unconsciously fulfill his mental image and direct the ball to the sand trap? He may want to miss it; he may try hard and use what he thinks is will power and effort. But his muscles don't know about this. All they know is to obey images. It is not their job to choose the images. They take it for granted the golfer will think where he wants his ball to go, not where he doesn't want it to go.

If you want to achieve your own legitimate goals, do not feel that satisfying accomplishment is impossible for you because you do not have the best body or the best brain. Use what you have. I sometimes tell athletes: "The instrument you're using isn't as important as the man who is using it." Learn to get the best out of your own instrument, and that will be good enough.

In short, relax and win.

Chapter Ten

Ways to Work without Fatigue

Work that we do willingly uses up much less energy than work that is done resentfully, or against our will, because, without realizing what we are doing, we use more effort when we force ourselves to do a job that we inwardly rebel against.

Sometimes we say that a person uses will power to make himself do disagreeable tasks, and some people consider the use of this will power virtuous. You often hear people say something like: "You have to hand it to Jones; he makes himself go through with it, whether or not he wants to." Notice the language that is used in describing Jones' actions. We say he forces himself against his will to do the disagreeable task. He is not willing to do it, but he does it anyway. Jones' actions would be much more admirable, and he would get more work done, with much less fatigue, if he would relax his resistance to his job; if he would really employ his will by becoming willing to do it. The effort that he now uses to force himself to do the job could be applied profitably to the job itself.

We can immunize ourselves against fatigue in our work if we learn how to form the habit of throwing ourselves wholeheartedly into what we are doing, with complete inward consent and with no mental reservations. It is impossible to work with rhythmic relaxation if we force ourselves to work without this inward consent. The work doesn't tire us nearly so much as our resentment against having to do it.

It is easy for people to tell you to get fun out of your work. But it is hard to get fun out of many jobs—mechanical ones like tightening nut number 23 on an assembly line all day long, for example. But if that is the kind of work you do, you can give such a mechanical job some personal meaning by associating it with some ultimate satisfaction to be derived from it, such as providing for your family, putting your children through college, or even buying yourself a new necktie. If you can think about the ultimate use to which your pay check will be put, it is possible to get satisfaction from even the dullest of mechanical jobs.

Actually the mere mechanics of *any* job are dull and uninteresting as things in themselves. It is not the motions one goes through, but what they mean to him, that makes a job, or even a sport, fun. Pulling a lever back and forth, over and over, while sitting in a cramped position is fully as monotonous as tightening nut No. 23. Yet I know any number of men who get fun out of these motions. They are college oarsmen. Find some larger meaning to tightening the nut, and you can get fun out of that too.

Some of today's leaders in business worked for years

on dull, routine jobs, without feeling frustrated, because they had some ultimate goal in view. Tightening a nut, or wielding a broom, had a larger meaning for them than the immediate results—securing a bolt or cleaning a floor.

Some people hate the work they have to do, but many people have the idea that any kind of work is a curse, a necessary evil, something to be avoided when possible. This mental image acts as a brake to the work image and causes muscle and nerve fatigue, mental confusion, and frustration. If you've got a job to do, don't run away from it, even mentally. If you must go one mile, be willing to go two. This relaxes away your emotional resistance to your work, and removes, at the same time, the primary cause of fatigue.

Just as there are many people who cannot give themselves wholeheartedly to their work because they hate their jobs, or because they resent having to do any kind of work, there are many more who find it impossible to give themselves wholly to their hours of recreation and rest. They never really quit working. These are the ones who carry their work home with them, and even to bed with them. This may be because they are really deeply interested in the work they are doing (so much so that they think they'd rather work than play), or it may be because they have certain fears and worries that keep gnawing at them and compelling them to work harder all the time. It is easier to work without fatigue if you like your work, but even if you do, taking your work into your leisure hours, taking it to bed with you, isn't such a good idea.

Get Rid of Fear and Worry

One of the negative images that tires us out by dividing our energies is fear. Many people are afraid to work hard because they think they will damage themselves by depleting their energy. Not everyone is as afraid of work as a man I know who told me: "My brother-in-law died on the job. Since then, I haven't had anything to do with work, because I decided it is dangerous." But many people are afraid to work at their full capacity because they think they have only a limited store of energy to draw upon. The late Dr. James Barbee used to have a stock answer for patients who complained to him that they were all run down. "You are wrong," he would say, "your real trouble is that you are all wound up."

What we need is release from the emotional tensions within us, rather than an additional supply of energy. Some people who have been told to relax and take it easy are afraid to spend themselves freely in their work or play. Relaxation does not mean holding yourself back, or putting on the brakes. Instead, it means free action, it means loosening the drive chain on your mechanism so that it can run free; it is the oil in your mechanism that cuts down on friction and drag; it is mental and physical free wheeling.

It has been reliably established that hard work in

itself never killed any business man. Galley slaves may
have died from overwork, but no business man today
runs that danger. What kills off young executives is not
overwork itself, but the fact that they have been working
with the brakes on.

Work that you do without emotional resistance does
not exhaust you. A mere fraction of the same amount of
work done under emotional strain can leave you exhausted for days. Moreover, the more energy you spend
purposively, the more your body creates. William James
was one of the first to comment on this phenomenon.
He wondered why it was that when a man speeded up
and stepped up his activities, he might suffer some fatigue
at the outset, but after a few days his mechanism seemed
to adjust itself to the new pace. James believed that very
few of us ever succeed in tapping the apparently inex-
haustible supply of energy within us.

Another emotional brake that tires us out is worry.
You cannot bring your full energy to a task if you are
worrying about the outcome. If you are worrying about
the outcome, you are holding failure images in your
mind. Unless these negative images are present it is impossible to worry. When our attention is focused upon
the possibility of failure, which is what happens when
we worry, our will is helpless and powerless to direct our
energy wholly towards our desired goal. The worry image acts as a brake, it drains off a part of our energy. We
then make an extra effort to overcome the brake, and

use up more vitality than it would take to do the job in the first place.

If you are an editor, and have a large batch of proofs to correct before the printer's deadline, don't keep worrying about the deadline and watching the clock. You'll make it, if you remember that the only way to do the job is to do it one word at a time.

Still another emotional brake that tires us out and keeps us from doing our best is the desire for perfection in our work—or even in our play.

I have found that perfectionism, or the unconscious attitude that one ought to be absolutely perfect, is a cause of tension in many people. The desire for perfection itself is not abnormal. We all want to be better and do better. And without this desire for improvement, mankind would probably still be back in the primitive stage of development. The sort of perfectionism I am talking about has nothing at all to do with the normal desire to improve ourselves, or to do a better job. Perfection is an ideal. It is a goal—something to shoot for. This is true whether we are considering learning athletic skill, developing our bodies, or mastering our jobs.

The normal person realizes that perfection is something out there in the distance, something to strive toward, and he uses it to set his sights by, and begins the journey from wherever he is. The perfectionist feels that he ought to be there already and he is impatient of the intermediary steps that could carry him there. He is somewhat ashamed of himself for not being there, and because he does not want to admit to himself or to others that he is not there, he refuses to take the steps that could carry him closer to the goal, and at the same time worries about it.

The perfectionist is tense because he must be forever on guard lest someone discover his imperfection. He has an egotistical mental image of himself as a perfect person, and he must avoid all situations that might prove his image false. Defeat or failure would destroy his perfection image, so to protect himself he just never begins. Some day he is going to write the great American novel, or go in business for himself, or do great things. But he keeps putting everything off to protect his pride; if he really got started, he just might find himself less than perfect. The perfectionist doesn't like to write letters, because they might turn out to be something less than perfect, they might not be literary gems. He is also a poor conversationalist. He is afraid to talk because he cannot be sure that everything he says will be clever, significant or important. If he would relax and write and say whatever comes to mind, he might surprise himself. If he would, as Somerset Maugham expressed it, "just take his pen in hand and let 'er rip," he might tap a creative flow.

Relaxed living—and working without fatigue—requires a certain amount of self-acceptance, self-respect, and self-approval. It helps remarkably in your work, and ultimately brings you nearer your goal, if you can bring yourself to surrender the desire to be perfect in everything now, and be willing to accept yourself as you are, where you are, and work in a relaxed way toward your goal.

There are many other things that act as emotional brakes, and keep us from working well and easily. You can, no doubt, think of many from your own experience. But whatever the brake is that may be burning up your energy, relaxation is the control lever that releases it.

I cannot emphasize too strongly the fact that muscular relaxation is the key to mental and emotional relaxation. Muscular contraction, or tension, and imagery go together. Stop the imagery and you stop the contractions in your muscles brought on by your mental images. On the other hand, learn to recognize the minute tensions in your muscles, and drop them, and you drop the imagery. You may not be able to see how training in passive relaxation can help you release emotional tensions in your work, but all I ask is that you practice the formula daily for a few weeks and judge the results for yourself.

Work When You Work—Play When You Play

A. F. Davis, Vice-President of The Lincoln Electric Company, Cleveland, Ohio, was ill when he was a young man and spent two years in a hospital, flat on his back. Today, though he is well past the mid-century mark, he is a regular dynamo. When he got out of the hospital, a wise doctor told him, "You can work hard, and play hard, but work when you work and play when you play." When we have work images and play images in mind at the same time, there is a perpetual tug-of-war going on. Just as the play image can put the brakes on your work, the work image can put the brakes on your rest. And one is as vicious as the other.

This does not mean that it is wise to work continuously for long periods without rest. But whether you are working in fifteen-minute shifts or twelve-hour ones, the principle of work while you work and play while you play holds true. While you're working, work.

Many people marveled at the boundless energy of Theodore Roosevelt. He was a man of action. But when he was not working he took advantage of every opportunity to rest. On his campaign trips he went to sleep on the train, and slept right up to the very minute when he had to go out on the back platform and make a speech. Edison also used this principle of concentrating completely on his work for a while, then taking a cat nap.

Rhythm in Your Work

Perhaps the best way to work without fatigue is the use of rhythm—alternate periods of work and rest. A tired worker puts forth more effort than a rested worker. Rest should not be considered a remedy for fatigue. It should be thought of as a preventive. When rest is used properly, there is no need at all to be tired.

Frederick W. Taylor, in an experiment at the Bethlehem Steel Works, proved that a rested worker can perform much more work than a tired one. In his book, *Principles of Scientific Management* (Harper and Bros., New York), he tells how he increased the amount of pig iron carried by laborers from 12½ tons a day to 47½ tons a day. Taylor picked out one man, who was then carrying an average of 12½ tons a day, and followed him around all day with a watch, instructing him to stop and rest at frequent intervals. Taylor never allowed this man to become tired, but forced him to rest before he got tired. The very first day this man carried 47½ tons of pig iron and was fresh as a daisy, while the other workers who had carried the usual 12½ tons were all worn out. Taylor's man had worked easily and carried 47½ tons; the other workers had worked hard and carried only 12½ tons.

Taylor proved that the easy way is the best way. Fatigue is not the sign of good work; it is a sign of inefficient work. The method of working that is best for our bodies is also the one that is best for getting the most work done.

Housewives can make good use of the principle of rhythm. Many housewives feel they do not have time to relax. Dr. Lillian Gilbreth is a well known Efficiency Engineer. Dr. Gilbreth, who raised twelve children by herself, after her husband died, and engaged in a professional career at the same time, didn't feel, while she was doing all this, that she didn't have time to relax. As an Efficiency Engineer she recognized that time spent in relaxation means time saved in the long run, and also promotes efficiency. She always takes short rests before she gets tired. If she has to lecture in the evening, she takes a short nap in the afternoon.

Typists, clerks, and all sedentary workers should find their own best rhythm. The rhythm of rest and work is different for each job and each person. No one can decide what your own best rhythm is but yourself, and you'll never know until you experiment. If you are working behind a desk, even two or three minutes of passive relaxation taken every 30 minutes or every hour can have a remarkable effect.

If your job requires that you stand on your feet most of the day, you should do a series of "tip toes," at least once an hour, to keep the blood from stagnating in your lower limbs. If you rise up on your toes ten or fifteen times, you will ease the blood vessels in the calves and keep fresh blood circulating. During the lunch hour, or whenever it is practical, you should passively relax, sitting or lying with your feet higher than your head.

To get the most out of rhythm, however, we should carry the principle right into the job we are doing. In the very doing of the job we can introduce a series of little rests. This is what the human heart does. It never takes a big rest; instead, it relaxes for a fraction of a second between each two beats.

If you have ever seen two experienced loggers sawing through a tree you have seen a good example of this continuous rest and work rhythm. The man whose turn it is to pull, pulls the saw towards him; he does not hold his arms up with his shoulder muscles. His pull against the saw holds his arms up. When he has finished his pull, he relaxes his arms. The other fellow then pulls both the saw and the first man's arms back to the starting position. Using this rhythm, a logger can saw all day long without becoming too tired. An inexperienced logger, who does not know the knack of the rhythm, can become exhausted in less than thirty minutes.

Many office machines have a lever that must be pulled down and released. If you have occasion to operate such a machine, try this: do not tense your shoulder muscle to hold your arm up; instead, grip the handle of the machine and pull directly against it. This pull in itself will hold your arm in position. When you have completed the forward pull, relax your arm, let the handle of the machine hold up your hand, and ride the handle back to the starting position.

Action followed by inaction is the proper way for the muscles of the human body to function. That is one of the reasons I have used the term, "rhythmic relaxation." Another reason is that the actions of the human body, when it is functioning as it should, can often remind us of poetry and music.

Many years ago, Grantland Rice made a movie short called "Rhythm," in which he showed slow-motion pictures of famous athletes in action. I had the pleasure of being included in the film. I was shown teaching rhythmic exercises to athletes at the U. S. Naval Academy. These slow-motion pictures showed that there was definitely something like music in the actions of champion swimmers, boxers, golf players, tennis players, and even men doing ordinary exercises as they should be done.

You can even feel this music in the actions of a good ditch digger. He will push the shovel into the dirt, grasp the handle near the shovel with one hand, and lift directly upward, close to his body. This is the most graceful way to lift an object, and also the easiest way. The ditch digger will then draw back with a swing, and swing—not push—the shovel full of dirt forward. At the completion of the stroke, he lets the shovel fall to the ground and drags it back to the starting position. There are no jerks or jumps in his movements.

It has been found that people get less tired if they hear music while they work. Laborers have known this for a long time. Laborers on docks sing and chant as they work. Oarsmen have always chanted as they work. Many times I have listened to the rhythmic grunts and groans of road gangs. Every soldier knows that it is less tiring to march when there is a brass band to march to. Rhythm automatically gets rid of unnecessary movements and excess efforts. For example, you simply cannot dance well, and be tense.

Be Lazy with a Purpose

  The time will come when the furrowed brow, the breathless expression, and the running back and forth will no longer be considered the marks of a hard worker. Instead, the boss will figure that he is paying for energy that is being wasted, and will resent it as he resents having a faucet left turned on, or having lights left burning all night.

When you are seated in a chair, give your whole weight to it. Don't act as if you were a sprinter waiting for the starter's gun; don't be ready to spring up at a moment's notice. Your leg muscles are not needed when you're sitting, so let them rest. Feel the pressure of the weight of your body against the chair seat. Give the weight of your feet and legs to the floor.

For a while, practice feeling the weight of your feet when you walk. When you open a door, feel the pull against your hand and arm. When you push against a door, feel the force of the direct push, and don't hold your shoulders rigid, but let them give a little. When you lift objects as light even as a salt shaker, or an ash tray, feel their weight, as if you were trying to judge just how much they weigh.

If you must do a lot of writing with a pen or pencil, become conscious of the drag of the pen on the paper, and the pressure of your fingers on the pen. Try to guess just how many pounds of pressure you are using to hold the pen.

This kind of practice teaches us to function with a minimum of effort. It also teaches us how to localize effort, teaches us which muscles are involved in a particular task, and thus enables us to relax those muscles which are not used.

How Distractions Tire You

My grandmother used the word distraction as a synonym for harassment, frustration, and fatigue. "I am distracted to death," she would say, or "I have just about reached the point of distraction."

Few of us realize just how tiring distractions can be. Noise tires us, even when we think we have gotten used to it. Several years ago, experiments were made to find out what effect a distracting noise would have upon typists. At first, their speed increased. In making an effort to concentrate in spite of the distraction, they overcompensated, and their typing improved. But the improvement was only temporary. Shortly, both speed and accuracy began to suffer. They made many more mistakes than usual. Our old enemy, excess effort, was doing its dirty work.

Paint companies have done extensive research to determine what effect distracting sights have upon the efficiency and fatigue of workers in industry. They have found that painting overhead girders a receding color, such as battleship gray, rather than a distracting color, such as bright red or yellow, increases production, cuts down the number of accidents, and lowers man-hours lost from such symptoms of fatigue as sick headaches, back pains, and eyestrain. Results along these lines have been so amazing that "Color Engineering" is fast becoming a major industry.

Disorder is a distraction that tires us far more than we realize. A disorderly desk makes for fatigue. Don't try to make an impression by having your desk piled high with things you won't be working on until tomorrow or next week. Get everything off the top of the desk except the immediate job, and you'll find that that job will go more easily and more quickly.

The housewife who has no order or plan is tiring herself without realizing it. It takes much less energy in the long run to have a place for everything and to put everything in its place.

Whatever your work is, learn to schedule it so that you can give your full attention to one job at a time. Don't allow a great many things to be pulling on your attention at the same time. Remember that the real villain in fatigue, as in most other personality ills, is excess effort. Whenever you find yourself getting unnecessarily tired, look for the excess effort you are putting into the job at hand.

If a situation has the power to make you expend excess effort, it has the power to fatigue you. To say that a certain person "makes me tired" is not a mere figure of speech. If he has the power to make you resist him, or attempt to use effort to change him or escape from him, he has the power to make you tired.

Chapter Eleven

How to Relax Away Your Fears

If, suddenly, you found yourself face to face with a grizzly bear, these are some of the things that would happen inside your body: your heart would speed up and pump more blood to your arms and legs—for fighting or running; your stomach would stop digesting food, and its blood supply would be sent to the muscles for reinforcement; you would breathe faster—giving more oxygen to the bloodstream, so that energy could be released faster; the adrenal glands would pour their hormones into the blood and literally give you a shot in the arm.

Under these conditions you could probably run faster than you had ever run in your life, if your predominant thought was to escape. If you were armed, and your predominant thought was to fight, you would probably fight harder than ever before in your life. We could say that your internal response to an external fear stimulus had been both adequate and beneficial. If you ran far enough and fast enough your muscles would discharge their tensions and there would be no left-over emotional tension. You would feel relaxed and relieved. A feeling of fear in a situation like this is normal and wise. But many tense people expect to come upon a figurative grizzly bear in ordinary, everyday situations. When this happens, fear becomes a problem.

The "X" Factor

Robert Ruark, writing of his experiences hunting lions in Africa, spoke of the "X" factor. The "X" factor was to him the mysterious, the unseen, the unknown, the general unattached feeling of fear in the situation that was over and beyond actual physical fear of the lion. The "X factor" is a good name for the non-existent grizzly bear or lion that so many of us see and respond to in ordinary situations.

"X" is the unknown factor. "X" is not a specific something that can be recognized and named. Consequently, you respond to it, not with a specific effort, but with a generalized effort, which makes for poor performance, lack of mental control over your physical machine, and tension.

It is "X" that gives you stage fright when you are called upon to give a speech. You are not actually afraid of the people in the audience. But the situation is a strange one (unless, of course, you make speeches regularly), and you respond not only to the actual elements in the situation, but also "X" which isn't there at all. Responding to "X" is what gives you butterflies in the stomach. You can discharge the tension in your muscles by your response to fear when there is a real danger present. But you can't discharge the tension generated by

"X." It stays inside to make you jittery. It is never our realistic fear response to actual dangers that causes us trouble; it is always either an over-response to a real danger, or a response to a danger that isn't there.

Fear Is Excess Effort

It has been pointed out before in this book that excess effort interferes with the mental and physical processes involved in the successful execution of any psycho-motor skill. We learned that making an excess effort did not help us to do better but had the opposite effect. Excess effort jams the machinery, and destroys our mental command over our physical machine.

It is easy to see then how fear of failure makes failure much more likely. For fear causes us unconsciously to put forth additional effort, at a time when we most need to be relaxed.

Let us take stuttering as an example. The stutterer is always afraid that he will stutter. The memory of past speech failures is fresh in his mind. He must not fail again. And so, without realizing it, he makes an extra effort to speak correctly. His effort, however, only succeeds in jamming the psycho-motor mechanisms involved in speaking. It freezes his speaking muscles and he unwittingly makes it impossible to speak fluently.

Ernest Douglass, head of the Speech Clinic of the Toronto Psychiatric Hospital, is a former stutterer. He uses the same method on others that he used to cure himself—to get over the fear of stuttering and stop trying so hard not to stutter. For the first month the patient is instructed to go out and make himself stutter, until he loses the fear of it and learns to stutter in a relaxed way. It is the things that a patient does to avoid stuttering, according to Dr. Douglass, that make him stutter.

In much the same way, fear of insomnia keeps us from going to sleep. Fear of being impotent makes many a man impotent. Fear of not being able to answer test questions causes the student's mind to go blank.

But it is always the excess effort put forth in response to the fear that does the damage. Relax, refuse to make the additional effort, and you render fear impotent. You will learn that in most situations "the only thing you have to fear is fear itself." And once you learn that you can conquer fear with relaxation, you need not even fear fear.

Often it is the memory of past failures that causes you to fear that you will fail in the future. Forget the past. Act as if success were inevitable, the task before you easy and well within your powers, and your fear will flee.

Most psychologists believe that the jittery feeling commonly known as stage fright is not a sign of personal inadequacy, but just the opposite. In case of emergency your mental and physical mechanisms send reinforcements to your muscles. If you can use these reinforcements, well and good. But if you have called up reinforcements when none are needed, or have called up more than are needed, you are in trouble. You use them against yourself.

Your stage fright is not a sign of inner weakness, but an inner surplus—over and above what can be used in the situation.

Fear is part of the body's defense mechanism and in itself is beneficial. It is good that we fear the automobiles on a busy street; otherwise we wouldn't survive very long. But while we might say that the person who has a healthy fear of automobiles and proceeds across a street with caution is using fear normally, there are people who are deathly afraid of automobiles. They shake and tremble if they get near an automobile, and wouldn't get in one on a bet. The person who looks carefully before crossing a street, and who always comes to a complete stop at railroad crossings, is responding in a normal way to actual and known dangers. His fear does not make his stomach churn, his heart flutter, and his blood pressure go soaring.

Tense, nervous people habitually call up far more reinforcements than they need. They need to take a lesson from the Texas Ranger who got off the train in a small Texas town and was greeted by the local constable with the question: "Where are the others?"

"What others?" asked the Ranger.

"I wired the governor we were having a riot. Don't tell me he sent only one Ranger."

"Why not?" asked the Ranger. "You have only one riot, haven't you?"

Fear of Pain

Pain, like tension and fear, is part of the body's defense mechanism. If your hand touches a hot stove accidentally, the resulting pain will cause you to jerk your hand away before too much damage is done. Pain is the fire-alarm system of the body. But the tense person's nerves magnify the alarm. They tell him there is a four-alarm fire when there is only a match to be put out. Numerous experiments have proved that when a person is relaxed he feels much less pain from a particular pain stimulus than when he is tense. Relaxation reduces his over-response, his over-defensiveness.

When I first enlisted in the U. S. Navy, some old sea dogs initiated me into their club. Part of the initiation ceremony consisted of heating an iron rod in my presence until it was white-hot, then stripping me to the waist and blindfolding me. Then the white-hot iron rod was placed against the bare flesh of my abdomen—or so I thought. The pain was excruciating (I can almost feel it now, just thinking about it). I could feel the hot iron searing my flesh. I could even hear it frying, and I could smell the burned flesh.

This is what actually happened: after I was blindfolded, one sailor pressed a piece of ice against my abdomen, while another pressed the hot iron against a piece of beefsteak. The pain I felt—as real a pain as I have ever experienced—came entirely from my mental image.

There was no painful stimulus present. How easy it is to understand, then, how a little genuine pain stimulus can be magnified many times by fear.

Relaxation makes any pain hurt less. Tension and fear distort the mental interpretation. You can prove this to yourself on your next trip to the dentist.

When the average person visits the dentist, he tenses up. He wishes he didn't have to go through with it; he wants to escape. And yet, as long as he is going anyway, the desire to escape serves only to create inner conflict, fear, and tension, and to make his pain perception more acute.

The desire to escape is a necessary part of the emotion of fear. If, when you are faced with a danger, your desire is to escape, you will feel fear; if your desire is to fight, you will feel anger; if your desire is neither to run away nor to fight, but to accept the situation as it is, you will not feel any emotion at all.

So, once you make up your mind definitely that you are going to the dentist, you can save yourself much fear and pain if you will give up all desire to escape. If you are actually going to run away from the dentist as you would from a grizzly bear, go ahead and feel afraid and become tense—it will help you run. But if you are not going to run, why play with the idea and get yourself all worked up about it? When you are in the dentist's chair, don't grip the chair arms and push downward against the footboard with your feet as you will be tempted to do. Instead, relax. Let the chair hold you up.

Give your attention to the weight of your body pressing down against the chair. You are not going to jump and run like a scared rabbit, so why let your muscles act as if you were? As the dentist goes about his various tasks, don't keep wondering if he's going to hurt you and hoping that he won't. Instead, keep telling yourself, "This will hurt, but I don't care. I don't give a darn what he does. I can take it, and I'm going through with it." If you do this you will feel no fear, and your sensitiveness to the actual pain will be very much lessened.

In other words, relax away your resistance to the situation, stop using your nerve force needlessly trying to make it not so. Be willing for it to be so. This does not mean that you must resign yourself to every negative condition or situation; it means that you are asserting your superiority over the situation, so that you can deal with it effectively.

Calling "X's" Bluff—Overcoming Fear

It is a generally accepted fact that we tend to fear the new or the unfamiliar, and that familiarity breeds contempt. This is true because we always see more "X" in a new situation. As we become more familiar with things, we tend to lose our fear of them, simply because we learn from experience what the situation actually is, and we can see for ourselves that "X" is the little man who probably wasn't there at all.

This is what happens when the awkward, frightened public speaker becomes poised after making many speeches. He has simply learned from experience that there wasn't anything to be afraid of. After he achieves assurance in public speaking, he may speak over the radio and get "mike" fright. Again he must learn somehow that there is no more "X" in a microphone than on a platform.

Most of us have experienced the feeling of relief and exhilaration that comes after something is done that we had long dreaded doing. "Why, there was really nothing to it," we say to ourselves. What we mean is that "X" failed to materialize. In other words, if you will do the thing you fear, the death of your fear is certain.

Doing the thing you fear just once may not banish the fear. In fact, you may become so excited about it that your worst suspicions will be confirmed. But if you will *gradually* expose yourself to "X," by degrees, you are bound to lose your fear. Use the same method that you would to condition your body to cold showers. By gradually making the water a little colder each day you can soon take a really cold shower without discomfort. When your doctor gives you a vaccine shot, he is giving your body a dose of weak germs to work on. Having overcome them, your body is then able to deal effectively with stronger ones. You can immunize yourself against "X" in the same way. If you are afraid to speak to large groups, start off speaking to small groups of a half-dozen people. If you are afraid of the very sight of a dentist's office—begin by making your first visit a social call.

In one way or another, you must arrange to expose yourself to "X" until familiarity breeds contempt, until you can carry the same relaxed attitude into the feared situation as you maintain in a safe situation.

Abraham Lincoln's advice to would-be public speakers who wished to obtain poise was to speak before the public as often as an opportunity presents itself.

When a Navy pilot crashes with his plane, he is sent up again immediately, if he is not hurt. In any case, he is taken up as soon as possible. Otherwise, he would very likely develop a full-blown case of "X" fright.

Complete muscular relaxation can achieve the same results as continual exposure to "X." During the Second World War I taught many Navy pilots to relax. Several times I had an opportunity to teach relaxation to pilots who had cracked up their planes and, due to injuries, were unable to be sent up again immediately. One of these pilots was grounded for more than thirty days. Yet he had no difficulty, and showed no fear, when the time came for him to fly again. He had learned how to relax his muscles. When he got in his plane he simply kept himself as relaxed as possible, and consequently made no excess efforts, or unnecessary responses to "X." On the other hand, I have known boys who had to give up flying after one crack-up because they did not know how to relax.

Psychologists say that we learn to fear certain

things. We become conditioned to respond in a certain way to a certain stimulus. It will help to overcome fear if we realize that the fear response is not something that must be. It is a learned response. When fear calls, we answer only because we have formed the habit of answering, and because we have thought that we must answer. But you don't have to respond.

Soldiers and sailors have an expression that shows they recognize instinctively that a man does have some choice in this matter. They call it "pushing the panic button." When one of their pals seems to be giving in to fear, they will tell him, "Just take it easy, Mac, and don't push the panic button." The trouble is that most of us have pushed the panic button too many times.

You can't use will power, effort, and force to fight fear, or to try to suppress the symptoms of fear by pretending to be calm. It is better, in most instances, to express fear when it is felt than to try to use force to cover it up. Remember that it is "X"—the fear of the grizzly bear that isn't there—that causes neurotic fear and anxiety. It is this neurotic fear, not healthy caution, that Dr. Grantly Dick Read was speaking of when he said: "Like an evil propaganda, its (fear's) destructive influence pervades the forces of human life. Were the man in the street to know the truth, its ravages would sound incredible. For my own part, after thirty years of close association with physical and mental derangements of health, I am persuaded, without a shadow of doubt, that with the exception of unforeseen accidents, the origin of every form of disease, both surgical and medical, whether hereditary or not, can be traced by careful investigation to the influence of fear upon the human mechanism." *

If your fear is real, there is always something you can do about it, some way to use your muscular energies that will relieve your tension. Or, if escape is impossible, you can learn to accept the situation. But if your fear is of "X," you can neither run away, accept the situation, nor fight back. Therefore, don't attempt to fight "X," or run away from it. Just do nothing; do not respond at all. You do not fear "X" because you respond to it; your response is your fear.

There are two ways to prevent this response. The way that is most useful in an immediate situation is to stop your muscles from responding. Contraction in a muscle is response; relaxation is absence of response. Here are some examples of immediate situations:

1. You are about to step up to the platform, or the microphone, to make a speech.

2. You are about to walk into a conference, and have some fears about its outcome.

3. You are about to be interviewed for a job that you are very anxious to get.

4. You are about to ask for a raise.

No doubt you can add to this list from your own experience.

The way that is most useful in a situation that is less

* *Childbirth Without Fear,* Harper & Brothers, New York.

immediate is to analyze the situation carefully. Sit down quietly, and write down on a piece of paper all the real dangers that you know will confront you. Take your time about this, and do it thoroughly. Don't minimize the real dangers, and don't be ashamed to put them into words. No one else is going to see the paper you're writing on. After you're sure you've covered everything, and know just what you have to face, then make up your mind that you will respond to these things only and be ready for them, and that you will not, at the last minute, respond to "X"—to the dangers that aren't there. Here are some examples of situations in which this technique can be useful:

1. You have an important letter to write, and are afraid of the impression it will make on the recipient because of certain things that must be said.

2. You are going to a party. There will be a lot of people there whom you do not know, and you're afraid you won't have anything to say. Remember that it will be the same for them!

3. You have an appointment next week with someone who can be important to your future, and you're afraid he may not like you.

Why don't you stop right now, and add to this list? In fact, think about your next important appointment— business or social—and try this technique on it now.

Relax, refuse to respond, and you will find that "X," the cause of all your neurotic fear and anxiety, will disappear into thin air.

Chapter Twelve

Learn to Let Go Your Bad Habits

The late Dr. Knight Dunlap made a life-long study of habits. His conclusions, though radical, were proved clinically in hundreds of cases. Dr. Dunlap found that the use of effort to cure a bad habit only made it worse. The more you try consciously to manipulate a subconscious process, the less likely you are to succeed. The more effort you make to go to sleep, the more likely you are to stay awake. The harder you try to put a tune out of your mind that just keeps going round and round in your brain, the less chance of success you have. The harder you try to force compulsive worry thoughts out of your mind, the more likely you are to worry.

Dr. Dunlap found, through experiments, that if you employed effort to forget, you increased your chances of remembering. If you made yourself consciously worry on purpose, you would be less likely to worry habitually. For years, Dr. Dunlap had made the error of writing the word "the" as "hte" on the typewriter. So he sat down and deliberately wrote "hte" several times, saying to himself all the while, "This is the way I don't want to write it." He never made that error again. Dr. Dunlap cured stutterers by having them deliberately and consciously practice stuttering; nail-biters by having them spend 30 minutes a day deliberately biting their nails; people with nervous facial tics, by having the patients practice the tic consciously before a mirror.

Though Dr. Dunlap's method may seem radical at first glance, it is consistent with the laws of learning. In fact, it was through his study of the laws of learning that Dr. Dunlap hit upon his method. We have control over our conscious acts, but no direct control over our involuntary nervous system. As any behavior pattern becomes conscious and voluntary, it becomes less subconscious and involuntary, and vice versa. By making a conscious effort to stutter, we automatically abandon all effort not to stutter. Thus Dr. Dunlap's negative practice is really a positive technique for relaxing our resistance to a certain behavior pattern.

Habit and Learning

Habit and learning are essentially the same. When we learn anything perfectly, it becomes a habit—we perform it automatically and without conscious attention. Tension and effort upset the subconscious mechanisms which are involved in learning. A little tension impairs learning, and a great deal of effort inhibits it altogether.

Dr. Albert Edward Wiggam, in his column, "Let's Explore Your Mind," referred to the experiments of Adolph Jost, German psychologist, who found that by going to sleep immediately after hearing a lecture or reading a book he could later recall more of what he heard or read than if he had stayed awake, and had tried to remember it all right away.

Max Sherover, President of The Linguaphone Institute, has carried this idea one step further. Several years ago, Mr. Sherover invented what he calls the "Dormophone," a phonograph with a time-clock. Material to be learned is recorded on special phonograph records. With the aid of the time-clock, the material is played while the listener is just dozing off to sleep, after he has gone to sleep, or just as he wakes up.

The Dormophone has been tested by several universities, and the results have been rather amazing. In one of the first experiments it was found that college students could memorize nonsense syllables in about one-fourth the time, if they were played over and over to them while they slept. Other experiments have shown that school children can learn their multiplication tables much quicker if they are played to them while they sleep. The learning of such things as foreign languages and Morse code can be greatly facilitated by the use of the Dormophone. Later experiments have shown that the Dormophone works just as well if the listener is awake, but completely relaxed.

The Dormophone is based upon the known psychological fact, established by earlier experiments, that learning is easier, and the things you learn stay with you longer, if you remain absolutely passive, make no effort, and attempt to make no response during the early stages of learning.

Children learn to speak by first listening to adults speak, and their speech mannerisms, inflections, and idioms, will reflect the speech they have listened to. Tumblers and other gymnasts learn skill much quicker if they first passively watch a good performer demonstrate perfect form; in fact it is practically impossible to learn tumbling without this training.

Dr. Wiggam reported recently that tests had shown that the best way for a pianist to learn to play a new musical composition was for him first to go over the entire composition in his mind before ever trying to strike a note on the piano. After this advance mental practice the student was then told to play the composition over a few times, slowly and easily, striking each note accurately, even if correct tempo had to be sacrificed at the beginning.

The important thing to remember is that any premature response on our part is apt to hinder rather than help learning. Until we know exactly what it is we are supposed to do, any doing on our part is likely to be wrong.

Know What You Want to Do

One important requirement in learning a skill, or in breaking or unlearning a habit, is to know exactly what it is you wish to do.

In New York City, an ex-alcoholic, Ed McGold-rick, operates "Bridge House," where he teaches alcoholics how to "unlearn" the habit of drinking. "Keep your thoughts on what you want to be or have in life," is his motto. The really big job, according to McGold-rick, is to get the alcoholic to visualize himself leading a satisfactory, happy life, free from alcohol. Most alcoholics, he believes, simply cannot conceive of a satisfactory, happy state of being in which alcohol has no part. When they think of giving up alcohol, they picture to themselves a life of deprivation, of suffering and craving, a dull, deadening routine with no excitements or satisfactions.

McGoldrick has his clients practice visualizing twice a day for thirty minutes at a time. In their mind's eye they are to picture a blank wall or screen. They are then to run a mental moving picture on this screen of themselves in the role they wish to attain. "In your mind's eye, see yourself as you want to be, doing what you want to do, looking as you'd like to look, with the job you'd like to have." The clients are told to see themselves living without alcohol and suffering no sense of deprivation because of it.

Knight Dunlap said, in *Personal Adjustment:* "If a response habit is to be learned, or if a response pattern is to be made habitual, it is essential that the learner shall have an idea of the response that is to be achieved, or shall have an idea of the change in the environment that the response will produce. . . . The important factor in

will power if he does triumph over these imaginery obstacles. A vicious cycle is set up. His increased efforts
convince his subconscious that the task must be difficult
indeed, and with the idea of difficulty reinforced, still
more effort is made. He becomes tense, and he finds
himself in the position of the man who said: "That I
would do, I do not, and that I would not do, that I do."

A man I know was ordered by his doctor to quit
smoking. For two months he tried and he suffered. He
would go for several days without smoking, then decide
to have just one. Then one day I noticed that he had not
smoked during the time I was with him, and I asked
him if he had managed to quit. "Yes," he said, "I haven't
smoked for a month, and it hasn't been so difficult. I decided one night that I was making too much of this
thing—that I was taking it too seriously. Without screw-
ing up my courage, or making any iron-jawed resolu-
tions, I just decided that I would not smoke the next
day, in much the same way that I might decide not to
smell any more violets. After the first day, I decided I
would go one more day—and it worked." Our will
works better when we are relaxed about the thing we
want to do.

Another reason that the use of will power so often
fails when we are trying to break a habit, or learn a skill,
is that we are apt to feel proud if we succeed and guilty
if we fail. The more the ego gets involved, the more the
learning of any skill is hindered. Any preliminary failures, errors, or backslidings—which are sure to come in

any learning process—often prove disastrous. The child who is learning to walk is not made to feel guilty or personally responsible when he stumbles or falls. The piano student suffers no loss of self-respect when he strikes a wrong note while he is practicing. And they go on to overcome their shortcomings.

One Step at a Time

Our efforts are often unsuccessful because we waste and weaken them by spreading them out over too much territory. Generalized efforts are nearly always ineffective. When we make an effort to do one specific thing, that effort is usually successful. Most of us, in deciding to give up a bad habit, resolve to quit for all time. This is a big job. The mere contemplation of it tends to keep us from attempting it. Our will cannot function tomorrow, and next week, or next month. It can function only now —in the present moment.

Alcoholics Anonymous makes good use of this principle when it advises its members not to try to give up drinking. That is too general. Instead, they are told to try not to take a drink today—during the next twenty-four hours. If we can let go of the past and the future, and live wholly in the present, we will find that our efforts are more productive. This does not mean that you should not look ahead, and plan for the future. Make all the plans you want. You must have some future goal at which to aim your present efforts. But do not try to carry out your plans until the time comes when you can do something specific about them. Relax and do your living in the present.

In his book, *Personal Adjustment,* Knight Dunlap said: "The potential damage of effort to stop the habit should be made plain to the patient. The principle that effort is useful only when applied to particular patterns of action should be explained to him; but that effort applied to a habit as a habit is detrimental. For example, when the desire or the urge for the practice comes on, he may think, 'I won't do it this time,' and may well make an effort to refrain; but he should avoid the desperate thought, 'I'll stop now and forever,' as a weakening generalization of effort." *

You cannot force your subconscious by will, but you can lead it with mental images. Relaxation helps you forget old habit patterns. You can then really turn over a new leaf, both physiologically and psychologically. You can start over and build new habits, in the same way that you learn any skill—through visualization, mental imagery, and relaxed doing.

'A Plan of Action

How can we put into practice the theory of relaxing away our habits? Following is a plan of action that I worked out many years ago as the best method of

* By permission from *Personal Adjustment,* by Knight Dunlap. Copyright, McGraw-Hill Book Company, Inc., New York.

learning athletic skills. Since learning and habit forma-
tion are the same, psychologically, I have also found this
plan of action to be effective for breaking bad habits or
learning new ones.

1. Know, first of all, just exactly what it is you wish
to do. To say that you want to quit smoking or to stop
biting your nails is not sufficient. Passively relax your
muscles. Then make mental pictures of your goal. Visualize, while relaxed, and not doing with your muscles or
your will, until you know just what the desired state is.
See yourself actually achieving the desired behavior pattern. See and realize just how you would feel and how
you would act if the new behavior pattern were already
an accomplished fact. At this stage make no attempt at
all to do anything to accomplish your goal. Until you
know what your target is, any shots you make are just
shots in the dark.

2. Do not attempt to force yourself into the new
role by will power. Instead, begin to imitate some person
who has achieved the goal you want to attain. Imitation
does not require effort, will power, and consciously con-
trived doing. It is relaxed doing. It is more subconscious
than conscious. When you imitate something you just
let yourself do it. Imitation also forces you to keep your
ideal goal in view, because you must imitate something.
It is impossible to just imitate generally. Truly to imitate you must become the thing you are imitating. It is
more a process of being than of doing.

3. Realize that your attitude about what you do is

just as important as the things you do. Keep your ego out of it. This is the only way you can profit by your mistakes instead of being devastated by them. Conceive of your progress toward your goal as a learning process. This takes the pressure off and allows you to begin relaxed doing toward your goal.

Plateaus, where no apparent progress is made, are typical of all learning. Errors advance you as much as successes, as long as you keep your goal in view. Realize this and do not feel any more guilty about an occasional backsliding than you would about an occasional fall if you were learning to ski. And if you decide in advance that you are not going to feel guilty about it, even if you fail, you increase your chances of not failing.

Knight Dunlap said that making a moral issue out of the learning of a new behavior pattern is the worst thing you can do. You must realize that the undesirable habit is undesirable, he believed, but you should think of it as being undesirable in the same way you think of a runny nose or chronic appendicitis as undesirable. The next worst thing you can do is to let your ego get mixed up in what you're doing to such an extent that you feel guilty after each slip-up or failure.

The laws of learning are the same for any behavior pattern you wish to learn. Approach the learning of a desirable personal habit the same way that you would approach the learning of a skill such as throwing darts, swimming, playing tennis, or piano playing.

4. Keep your efforts, or your conscious will, pin-

pointed on the things you can do right now. Don't worry about whether or not you will do them tomorrow. You can't live tomorrow today.

If you resolve to take a walk every day, not to speak unkindly to your family, to get more sleep from now on, you are very likely to fail. If, instead, you say: "I shall take a walk today, I am not going to speak unkindly to my family now, I am going to bed early tonight," you are much more likely to succeed.

Ironically enough, we already use this method unconsciously when we are forming or maintaining an undesirable habit. No one says to himself: "I am going to drink excessive amounts of whiskey for the rest of my life." Instead, he says: "I'll take just this one," or "This one won't hurt me," or "This one won't count." The unconscious efforts we make to form bad habits are always specific, never general. And so we form these habits because we are following the laws of learning. If we want to be successful in breaking the habit, which in effect means learning a different behavior pattern, we must follow these same laws of learning.

5. When positive practice in the new behavior pattern seems to be difficult and unrewarding, switch to negative practice if it is possible. Negative practice should not be tried by one's self on such habits as drinking, dope addiction, etc. but in the hands of a psychiatrist, skilled in its use, it can even be of benefit in overcoming these habits. To overcome such harmless habits as stage fright, sleeplessness, nail-biting, and so on, you may use

negative practice all you like. Often only one or two sessions of deliberately trying to make yourself feel as scared as possible when addressing an audience will relieve your stage fright almost completely. Dr. Albert Edward Wiggam suggests that you can even use your negative practice on stage fright without actually facing a strange audience. Practice feeling afraid before members of your own family. Stand up before them and pretend that you are making your speech before a crowded auditorium, and see how much stage fright you can develop.

It all boils down to the fact that you learn better and faster when you are learning and practicing without any sense of inner pressure, tension, or compulsion. Your mental and physical servants work better for you when you take the pressure off them.

Chapter Thirteen

Tension and Human Relations

Fear is catching. When a deer runs wildly through the wood, other animals become frightened. Although they do not perceive the danger, the fear in the deer alerts them to danger. This is a survival mechanism which operates in humans too. When we feel that another is afraid, our primitive subconscious tells us, "Watch out! You'd better be afraid too!"

John E. Gibson, writing in the March, 1951, issue of *Everywoman* magazine reported how twenty-two psychiatrists took on the fears of nervous patients by merely listening to sound recordings of the patients discussing their fears. At the beginning of the test the psychiatrists were calm. They were all stable personalities. But in a short time they felt nervous and anxious. They "caught" the fears of their patients.

Why does an infant become nervous and upset when its mother is frightened? Why is it that a calm, relaxed person can quiet a nervous baby with soothing talk even though the baby cannot understand a word that is said? There is something calm and relaxing in the tone of voice, the mannerism, or some facet of the personality, that does get across to the other person, whether we will it or not. The presence of some people has a therapeutic effect on us, and other people seem to upset us, to make us tired, merely by being around.

But the important thing to remember is that relaxation is just as contagious as tension. And if you can stay relaxed yourself, you can make yourself immune from the fear and tension of those around you, and help them to catch your relaxation. William James said once that if you achieve harmony and calmness in your own person, you may be sure that a wave of imitation will spread from you, as surely as the circles spread outward when a stone is dropped into a lake.

Not long ago I heard a psychiatrist tell a study group that he believed that nervousness is "inherited" by our children in just the same way that they happen to inherit some of our physical characteristics, the language we speak, and our accents.

Relaxation in the Home

Children catch their feelings from their parents. Your children demonstrate your own inner tensions in their actions, even though you think you are disguising them and keeping them in check. The first step in getting children to relax is to learn to relax yourself. You will then find that their naughtiness does not get on your nerves as it did before.

Reading the formula to children can be extremely rewarding. Most of them take to it readily, especially if you present it in the form of a game. Young children like to play "let's pretend." The formula can be made more attractive to children if you tell them: "Let's pretend you are a mechanical man whose screws and joints are all too tight, and that I am going to loosen them all up."

There are many innovations that can be used to teach children how to relax specific muscles. If you want a child to relax his arm, for example, you can tell him to pretend that he is a little bird with a broken wing. Or, he can be a cowboy who has been shot in the shoulder, so that his arm is useless and flops of its own weight when you lift it.

When you want a child to reduce his breathing cycle, he can be told to pretend that there is a candle held just before his lips, and that he is breathing so easily and gently that his breath does not blow the flame out—in fact does not even cause it to flicker.

Imagery, or step three in the formula, can be presented to the child in the form of a story. Populate your story with all the people and creatures and things that appeal to a particular child's imagination. Take care to see that your word story is visual—that you talk in terms of things seen. Also, see to it that your story is wholly pleasant. Unpleasant visual images are tensing; pleasant images are relaxing.

Most of the time, children are bad because they are over-tired. Contrariness, bad temper, and other naughty traits often disappear when the child becomes rested.

At Boys' Ranch, Texas, I had a chance to see the effects of relaxation on young boys. The results were enough to convince me that relaxation has a role to play in child training that goes beyond mere physical training. Experts in the field of juvenile criminology have said that a feeling of hostility against society is the key to juvenile delinquency, and that the child's efforts to defend himself against what he considers a hostile society is the clue to the delinquent behavior.

For example, Dr. David Abrahamsen, psychiatrist at Columbia University, made a four-year study of criminals. He found that half of them suffered from indigestion; they also suffered from skin trouble, respiratory diseases, heart trouble and nervousness. His study indicated that these physical ills could be traced to tension. "Family tension breeds criminals," Dr. Abrahamsen says. He goes on to say that bickering and nagging in the home cause children to tighten up with resentment and hostility, which result in their rebellion against authority, and their response to the will of the gang.

Dr. Benjamin Spock advises parents to relax, enjoy and, most of all, to love their children. To this, Dr. Ruth Barbee, director of the Family Relations Institute, Atlanta, Georgia, adds: "To really love your children in a dynamic sort of way, you must relax with them. One of the healing principles of love is acceptance. You cannot give your child a feeling of acceptance when there is a barrier of tension between you."

If you can relax yourself and teach your child relaxation you will do much for his character and his health. It is common knowledge that we are more apt to fall prey to some physical disease, even the common cold, during those periods when we are under a mental strain, or when we are physically fatigued.

Why is it that polio often strikes the most active children, even college athletes? Why is the incidence highest among children in the hot summer months, and among college football players in the early winter months? My personal opinion is that fatigue, with its resultant nervous exhaustion and lowered vitality, presents the ideal medium for polio to thrive in. Many case histories show that the patient became ill immediately after a long swim in cold water. The buoyancy of the water, plus the stimulation of its coldness, often creates an illusion of vitality and masks fatigue, until the swimmer emerges to find himself all worn out.

At present I am engaged in a one-man campaign to interest the mothers of America in a very simple program which I believe might materially reduce the number of polio cases:

1. See to it that your child does not become excessively chilled.

2. See to it that your child does not exert himself, especially in summer, to the point of exhaustion. Do not forbid swimming, nor exercise. When not carried to the point of exhaustion, exercise builds body vitality.

3. During mid-spring and all through the sum-

mer, provide a rest period of at least thirty minutes in mid-afternoon, during which the child
either lies quietly in bed, or takes a nap.

4. Seek to maintain a wholesome, relaxed attitude
in the home so that your child is not under the
burden of emotional strain.

Relaxation in Business

A relaxed person makes you feel better. You subconsciously catch some of his relaxation. His relaxation
seems to tell your subconscious that he is a friend instead
of a foe. An enemy is tense and aggressive when he faces
you; a friend has his defenses down.

When I was on the staff at Bill Brown's Health
Farm, a New York City businessman confided to me
that he was very much troubled by the fact that he had
never been able to get on well with strangers. Because he
realized his weakness, he worked inside as much as possible, and had men working under him who had the
personality to get on well outside. This man's personality
showed the typical tense pattern. His speech was hesitant
and reserved. He carried his shoulders so tensely that he
often complained of aches and pains in the back of his
neck at the end of the day. He slept badly.

No mention was made of relaxation as a possible
cure for his personality problems, but he was induced to
practice the formula so that he could improve his sleeping habits and conserve his energy during the day. About

a month later he told me that he was sleeping better and was less tired at the end of the day. "But more important," he said, "I think I am becoming a more likable person. I find I am more at ease with people. I don't dread talking to strangers. And people seem to take to me better."

Here are some things to remember if you want to get along better with strangers:

1. Relax your shoulders and your jaw. Tensed, hunched shoulders are defensive and arouse defensiveness in others. A tight, determined jaw scares people.

2. Most of the people you will meet want to be friendly. As a working hypothesis, assume that everyone you meet is going to be friendly, and do not erect subconscious defenses against imagined hostility. Relax, and don't approach people mentally with your left out and your fist doubled.

3. A smile has a relaxing effect on the other person as well as on yourself. When you smile, it indicates to the other fellow that your intentions are friendly and that he need not erect any defenses against you.

4. Don't be an eager beaver. Don't strive and strain to impress people. Relax, and see whether or not they are going to impress you.

5. Don't make an effort to get the other fellow to relax. Just keep relaxed yourself. Tense muscles and strained faces give the impression that we are going to spring at the other person, mentally, if not physically. Sit

solidly in your chair. Let your balled fists, which are sym-
bols of hostility, relax.

Doctors, nurses, teachers—relax!

Doctors, nurses, teachers, and all people who are in
a position to advise, can benefit those who come to them
for help, by relaxation. Dr. Grantly Dick Read, in his
book, *Childbirth without Fear,* says: "Unfortunately, it
is not recognized how the opinion of the medical man is
understood by the patient not only in health but in disease, without any word to communicate his feelings.
There is an atmosphere; there is an unexpressed
thought, and apart from that, there are those psychological influences which are conveyed from mind to mind by
some mystic method of which we are at present unaware.
There is, none the less, no doubt whatever that from one
person to another a very definite influence is conveyed.
Confidence is imparted or fear is awakened, and although the patient may enter the consulting room in a
state of anxiety—as indeed all patients do to a greater or
lesser extent—it is that mystic something which the
physician conveys, not only in his manner, but in his
personality, which formulates the end result of the con-
sultation." *

We are very susceptible to the feelings of those
whom we regard as authorities in their field. This is
especially so when the authority's opinion has some bear-

* Harper and Brothers, New York.

ing on our personal welfare. It does no good if a tense and anxious nurse or doctor puts on a superficial smile and tries to convince the patient that everything is all right. If you are worried about the patient's condition, this is conveyed to him, and the fact that you are taking pains to try to hide your worry only makes him suspect that he is sicker than he really is.

It will help if you will remember that tension is required to feel fear, anxiety and hostility. You must even tense your muscles in order to feel a dislike for a person. You cannot feel fear, hostility, or anxiety, and you cannot convey these feelings, when you are thoroughly relaxed. You do not need to remember a thousand and one things to do and not do. All you need to do is to relax your muscles—and keep them relaxed. When tenseness goes, all the negative factors that accompany tenseness go also.

Relaxation and Marriage

Marriage requires more fine adjustment than almost any other human relationship.

Dr. Ruth Barbee, Director of the Family Relations Institute in Atlanta, Georgia, is nationally known for her success as a "marriage doctor." Dr. Barbee believes that if a husband and wife can relax together they will strengthen every bond between them. She especially recommends a period of relaxation when the husband comes home from work, and says: "Coming home from work should be a happy, pleasant occasion, when husband and wife can sit down and relax together, enjoy a cup of coffee or tea before dinner, listen to records, or just have fun talking together. This should be a period of transition during which both husband and wife can shed the tensions of the day, and reorient themselves for the evening hours. Too often the husband carries the worries and tensions of his work home with him, and the wife carries over the accumulated tensions and problems of housekeeping into their evening hours. Both should reorient themselves for a different kind of experience during their hours of recreation, and relaxation provides the atmosphere for this reorientation."

Dr. Barbee says also that all marital troubles can be traced to tensions of various kinds. Here are some suggestions from her as to the ways of using relaxation in marriage:

1. Learn the art of relaxing your muscles, and thereby relax your emotional tension.

2. Maintain a relaxed attitude toward your marital partner. "You hold a husband or wife with an open hand," she says. Dr. Barbee believes that if you try to put a figurative ball and chain on your partner you will lose him or her, and that even if your marriage doesn't end in divorce, you'll lose your partner's affection and respect. Let him feel free, not enslaved by your tense efforts to hold on to him, or to make him the sort of person you feel he ought to be.

3. Remember that love cannot be forced or coerced by making efforts. It comes. Love which can be demanded or forced ceases to be love. Relax from all efforts to make the other person love you, and concern yourself with your own capacity to love. If you can do this, love will come to you as a sort of reflex action.

4. Relax from your efforts to domineer, or to prove yourself superior to your marital partner.

Dr. George Humphrey of Queens College, Montreal, reports that he used relaxation as a sort of "love charm" to repair marriages that were on the verge of breaking up. Several of his patients told him that they had fallen out of love with their mates, or that their mates had acquired the capacity for irritating them to the point of distraction. Dr. Humphrey's prescription was to have the husband (or wife) sit in an easy chair, take three deep breaths, let them go with a sigh, and then consciously let go their muscles one by one until they were thoroughly relaxed and in a somewhat drowsy, dreamy state of mind. While in this drowsy, relaxed state they were asked to call up mental images of their mates —not as they had been picturing them, but as they would like them to be. If a man had been harassed by what he considered his wife's nagging, he would think of her as being understanding, considerate, and affectionate.

It is a well known fact that everyone has both good and bad qualities, and that we generally see what we look for. During courtship, lovers are proverbially blind to each other's faults, and thereby tend actually to bring out the best in the other person. It is also a well known fact that people have a tendency to be what we think they are and expect them to be. Dr. Humphrey would have his patients go back in memory to their courtship days and think of their partners as they thought of them at that time. After three or four of these sessions, his patients reported to him that they had fallen in love all over again with their mates—and that their marital partners were much more affectionate and understanding!

Some Ways to Achieve Relaxed Human Relations

Laughter relieves tensions. People who laugh easily are relaxed persons. And people who can learn to laugh more become more relaxed. One good laugh together between two persons can do more to mend strained personal relations than hours of intellectual reasoning.

Not long ago, I witnessed, in a minor street accident, the relaxing power of laughter. Two automobiles had a slight collision at an intersection, and one shiny, new fender was dented. The two men emerged from their cars at the same time and, for a moment, the atmosphere was tense and strained. In a case of this kind the natural tendency is for each person to go on the defensive and try to prove that it wasn't his fault. Once an argument of this kind starts, it is difficult for either party to give ground. But in this case, the man whose car had the dented fender cleared away the tension with a good hearty laugh. "How will I ever explain that to my wife," he laughed, "when I have been warning her every day not to smash the fenders?" The other man then laughed also, and offered to pay for the damage, although there was some doubt as to whether the accident was his fault.

Remember the relaxing power of laughter in any situation that is on the verge of becoming tense and strained. You can nearly always find something to laugh at in any situation. Most of us take life in general, and our own problems in particular, much too seriously.

Psychologists define laughter as a "superior adjustment within the individual." To be able to laugh at anything you must feel superior to that thing. When you learn to laugh at your mistakes, instead of brooding about them, something within you becomes superior to your mistakes. When you learn to laugh at yourself, something within you becomes superior to the bumbling, egotistical, self-centered part of you that got you into trouble in the first place.

Ed Miles, sports writer for the *Atlanta Journal,* wrote an article in which he said that Mrs. Frank Kibbler won the Atlanta City Golf Tournament for Women "by a giggle." Her secret, according to Miles, was that each time she made a mistake, or landed in the rough, she laughed about it, and remained relaxed. Her opponent took her own mistakes too seriously and became tense. The relaxed Mrs. Kibbler therefore won "by a giggle."

Abraham Lincoln, who knew the power of laughter, was once taken to task by a serious-minded cabinet member for his unseemly levity at a time when conditions were so very serious. President Lincoln, who usually opened cabinet meetings by telling a joke, replied, "Without a few minutes of laughter each day I should go mad."

Another way to maintain relaxed human relations is to refrain from talking about all your troubles with everyone you meet. Remember that unpleasant mental images bring tension and pleasant mental images bring relaxation.

If you are inclined to be super-critical, it may help you to relax to learn that a group of psychologists found, after studying hundreds of case histories, that critical, chronic fault-finders are more tense and nervous than people who are more tolerant of the faults of others. Their prescription, which worked like magic on those who tried it, was: "Stop finding fault."

This doesn't mean that you have to become intellectually blind. It does not mean lowering your ideals, nor condoning evil. It does not mean shutting your eyes to the faults of others. But it does mean shutting your heart to their faults. Sydney Smith once remarked that even though we are not able to make ourselves avoid seeing the faults of others, we don't have to hate people for their faults.

The critical person reacts emotionally to the faults of other people, to the imperfections in situations. Many people become emotionally upset and tense because some person they are closely associated with has some irritating mannerism. You do not need to approve your friend's nail-biting, knuckle-cracking, finger-drumming, ear-pulling, teeth-sucking, or gum chewing, but you do not need to allow the irritating mannerism to make you tense. You can immunize yourself against tension of this sort by deliberately letting your body become heavy and relaxed. Let your jaw hang loose; let your shoulders droop; unclench your hands. It is not really the mannerism that makes you tense; it is your reaction to it, your fighting it inwardly, that does the damage. Relax, and stop fighting against it. If you can learn to accept people emotionally as they are, with all their faults and shortcomings, it will do much to remove tension from your life.

A friend of mine has a job that requires almost constant travel by automobile. He tells me that when he first took this job he became so irritated and tense over the bad manners of other motorists that his doctor told him he must find some way to relax or give up the job. "I discovered a secret that worked like magic for me," he said. "Before I discovered this secret I would blow up when someone honked his horn behind me at a red light, just as the light turned amber. When I met a road-hog, my blood pressure soared. But now it all pours off me like water off a duck's back."

His secret? "I decided," he said, "that there were a certain number of ill-mannered, rude so-and-so's in the world; that there was nothing I could do about it, and that I wasn't responsible for it. After that, when I encountered one of these individuals I just said to myself 'there's another one of them,' in much the same way as I might take notice of a stunted tree, or a sick dog. I don't approve of stunted trees or of sick dogs. But neither do I get mad at them for being as they are."

Chapter Fourteen

Relax and Stay Young

Our bodies were not meant to deteriorate or waste away when we get to be fifty, sixty, or seventy. There is a common belief that we grow old and are unable to function properly because the structure of the body has a tendency to wear out with the passage of time. But instead of saying that function is impaired by structure, we would be nearer the truth if we said that structure is impaired by function. Physiotherapists claim that function builds structure. Relaxation enables our bodies to function as they should. Proper functioning helps to maintain and rebuild the proper structure.

Dr. Raymond Pearl of Johns Hopkins University has said that a man of seventy is composed of very little, if any, of the same material substance that he was made of when he was twenty. "Probably," says Dr. Pearl, "there is not a single molecule in him at seventy that was there at twenty."

For the past ten years, the new science known as gerontology has made an extensive search for the fountain of youth. And while gerontologists do not claim to have found the secret yet, they have narrowed down the search. They tell us that the real fountain of youth is within the human body itself. Old age is no longer regarded as normal, but as a pathological condition. Aging is a biological, not a chronological, process, they tell us. Time itself is not deadly. The condition, formerly called senescence, is not caused by time, but only occurs in time. All the so-called symptoms of old age may be found in any age group—even in infants. No two people age at the same rate; one may be old at forty; another may be young at seventy. The biological phenomenon that we have called old age is more likely to be found in old folks, not because of their chronological age, but because the pathological conditions of the body have been going on for a longer time, and have progressed further, than in the chronologically young.

Dr. Ernest P. Boas, of the College of Physicians and Surgeons, Columbia University, writing in the *American Journal of Orthopsychiatry* (January, 1940), said: "I believe that although aging may play a part in the phenomena of arteriosclerosis and of hypertension, there must be other and probably more significant factors governing their development. Recognition of this has very practical implications; it leads us not to accept the so-called degenerative disorders of middle life as evidences of the inevitable wearing out of the body mechanism, but to regard them as disease states, to search for their causes, and to seek methods of prevention and treatment."

Is Aging Inevitable?

The phenomenon known as aging is not inherent in the living cell. The most simple type of animal—the protozoa—shows no signs of the alleged poisoning effects of time. Dr. Alexis Carrel placed a slice of embryonic chicken heart in a laboratory glass dish, fed it with blood plasma, and washed away the accumulations of toxins. This tissue did not grow old. After some 35 years, Dr. Carrel said that the cell colonies remained indefinitely in the same state of activity, that they did not record time qualitatively and that they were, in fact, immortal.

Dr. L. V. Heilbrum, zoologist and physiologist at the University of Pennsylvania has said that in the case of some lower animals—flat worms, for example—it is possible to make older animals grow young again. Man's body is made up entirely of cells of essentially the same type that have been kept young, and have even been made to grow biologically younger, in the laboratory. Why is it that the biological time clock can be stopped, or turned back, in the simpler forms of life, and not in human beings?

Dr. Leo Loeb, who pioneered in tissue cultivation in the laboratory, answers that question by telling us that aging is not inherent in the individual cell, but that it is only the fate of the more complicated organism in which different types of cells and tissues are dependent upon each other.

This gives us the clue. It used to be said that a man is as old as his heart. Then someone discovered that in order to keep the heart young, the kidneys must be kept young, so he said that a man is as old as his kidneys. When someone else discovered that the ductless glands must operate properly to keep both heart and kidneys young, he said that a man is as young as his glands. Bogomolets found that the connective tissue had to function properly in order that all the organs should function properly, so he said that a man is as old as his connective tissue. And still the final answer eluded the scientists. As soon as one of them found an organ of the body that seemed to hold the secret, another scientist found that some other function influenced this organ. The search for the scientific fountain of youth continued to be a will-o'-the-wisp, as frustrating as Ponce de León's fruitless search, until Dr. Hans Selye, of Montreal (who pioneered in the use of ACTH and cortisone), came up with his "unified concept."

According to Dr. Selye's theory, when any organ of the body is attacked by any outside source, whether it be emotional stress, virus, or bacteria, the body as a whole reacts—not just the organ under attack—as a unit to defend itself. But it frequently happens that in attempting to defend itself, the body overdoes it and over-defends itself. Dr. Selye believes that what we call disease is a condition that results, in one way or another, from the body's inadequate defense of itself.

For example, Dr. Selye discovered that the body's

method of defense in arthritis, and many other diseases, is as follows: a certain area of the body is attacked; certain nerves carry word of this attack to the pituitary gland at the base of the brain; the pituitary then begins to organize for defense by secreting a hormone which stimulates the adrenal glands to secrete still another hormone; this adrenal hormone goes to the area under attack, and provides it with the needed material to fight back, or to organize defenses, or both. However, at the same time, the pituitary secretes another hormone (ACTH) which in turn stimulates the adrenal glands to secrete still another hormone (cortisone). Cortisone accompanies the fighting hormones and acts as an overseer to keep them from getting out of hand; without cortisone to restrain them, they run riot and cause the body literally to defend itself to death. Dr. Selye believed that the condition known as arthritis was the result of the body's over-defending itself, possibly because there had been an insufficient supply of cortisone present.

If that was the reason, then Dr. Selye decided that injections of cortisone, which would tone down the body's defense system, should prove beneficial in arthritis. Experiments showed that this was true. Later, it was found that ACTH, which stimulated the body to secrete its own cortisone, had essentially the same effect. This is why one drug, either cortisone or ACTH, has been found beneficial for the treatment of a wide variety of ills, apparently unrelated. For example, ACTH has been found to have value in the treatment of asthma, burns, inflammation of the eye, and many other conditions. According to the unified concept, all of these various ills are brought about by the body's over-defense in the pituitary-adrenal mechanism.

The body defends itself in different ways against different attacks, and the results of over-defense are also varied. The use of anti-histamines against colds and hay fever is based on the same principle. When mucous membranes of the nose, throat, and bronchial tubes are attacked by dust, pollen, or other foreign matter, the body manufactures a chemical known as "histamine." Histamine stimulates the membranes to secrete mucous to throw off the invader. A Navy doctor believed that the condition we call a cold is simply an excess secretion of this mucous substance. The runny nose is not caused by a cold, he believed; a runny nose is a cold. He reasoned that an anti-histamine substance should keep the body from over-defending itself against mucous membrane invaders and thus cure a cold.

Dr. Selye and other doctors are now engaged in research to try to discover other ways in which the body over-defends itself, and to develop methods of therapy to fit additional diseases. In the meantime, Dr. Selye advises laymen that they can begin to take advantage of his discoveries by learning to relax.

In 1947, Dr. L. Friedland of Paris, France, reported a number of medical experiments which seem to strengthen Dr. Selye's theory further. According to an article in *Magazine Digest,* Dr. Friedland reported that a number of diseases had been treated successfully by using anaesthesia to stop the body's nervous system from fighting back and over-defending itself. Dr. Friedland is quoted as saying, "Where there is no reaction, there is no disease. The reaction is not a protection against the disease, but the disease itself."

Doctors Thomas H. Holmes, Helen Goodell, Stewart Wolf and Harold G. Wolff of the New York Hospital, and Departments of Medicine and Psychiatry at Cornell University Medical College, recently reported their belief that many nasal and sinus troubles could be traced to emotional conflicts. An emotional conflict which caused the patient to go on the defensive, they said, caused swelling and obstruction of the nasal passages.

What has all this to do with relaxation and long life? Simply this: Dr. Selye's discoveries, and the findings of many other scientists, point to the fact that all diseases are caused, in one way or another, by the body's reaction to stress, in one form or another. Dr. Selye does not recommend relaxation as a magic cure-all. To regard it as such could be dangerous, since it might cause you to forego needed emergency medical treatment. If you have an infected throat, appendix, or any other disease, you would be foolish indeed to attempt to relax it away. When stress has gone so far as to cause sickness and physical injury, you need emergency medical help before you can be in a position to help yourself. The medical doctor is in a position to overcome the immediate effects of stress and to give you another chance to live in a less strained way. Even when you are not sick, regular physical check-ups should be part of your routine. If stress has started to make inroads on your health, your doctor can help to put you back on your feet.

But if relaxation cannot be regarded as a cure, it can be justly considered as a preventive of both old age and disease, and as a valuable adjunct to medical therapy. Dr. Arnold Hutschnecker points out in his book, *The Will to Live* (T. Y. Crowell Company, New York), that ACTH and cortisone do not cure disease, remarkable as their effects may be. They perform a valuable function in removing, for the time being, the effects of stress. And unless the effects of stress are removed for us, we cannot help ourselves. After the damage is done we cannot cure ourselves by relaxation. For this we need penicillin, ACTH, cortisone, and other medical therapy to help restore the damage, to stop the course of destruction, and to give us another chance. But Dr. Hutschnecker says further that there is no form of medical therapy that will cure us permanently until we develop more wholesome and realistic ways of meeting stressful situations in our lives.

Relax for Beauty

"Youth is not a time of life, it is a state of mind. People grow old only by deserting their ideals. Years wrinkle the skin, but to give up enthusiasm wrinkles the soul." So says Charles Forrer, District Manager of Washington National Insurance Company. He might have added that tension wrinkles the skin more than years do. Dermatologists have found that long, continued tension actually shears away the fat deposits underneath the skin of the face.

Doctors Thomas S. Szasz and Alan M. Robertson, of the University of Chicago, have found that sustained tension in the jaw and scalp muscles can cause baldness, by pinching the blood vessels that feed the scalp. They found that men with serious, taut, facial expressions were most affected by premature baldness.

We do not want to go through life with the smooth faces of youth. Wrinkles, in themselves, do not detract from beauty. The smooth face of youth is an open page; wrinkles that form on the face from laughter, maturity, experience, and character enhance the charm of the page; wrinkles from tension, fear, and doubt mar it.

Marlene Dietrich's secret of glamour is "plenty of soap and water and an untroubled mind." Even the most classic and perfect physical features cannot be really attractive if they are burdened with fear, tension, and anxiety. And there is something charming and attractive about even the most ordinary features, if there is something behind them that is calm, relaxed, and untroubled.

Another way to look young is to feel young. An Englishman told me that during Winston Churchill's election campaign many of his associates were surprised to see that at the end of the day, when Churchill was weary and let down, he looked like an old man. But, after a bath and a few hours' sleep, the old enthusiasm for living would return, and Churchill would seem to have shed ten years or more before again appearing in public. It is your enthusiasm, your faith, your zest for life, and your will to live that make you appear either young or old to the other person.

I, too, have seen a man age ten years in a single night after a particularly humiliating defeat that left him nothing to live for; and I have seen both men and women shed ten years in as short a time, when some event or circumstance gave them back some zest for life.

It is your posture, your walk, the tone of your voice and your mannerisms, rather than your purely physical appearance, that advertise you as old. If you walk with a beaten, faltering, fearful step, if your shoulders are hunched from carrying the cares of the world, if your voice is tired and old, if your mannerisms are fussy and nervous, rather than dominant and alive, you are advertising to the world that you are an old person, regardless of your chronological age. More than that, you will feel old.

Straighten your shoulders, hold your head high, raise your chest, breathe deeply, and step out with a firm and confident step, as if you had somewhere important to go, and your behavior will begin to make you feel younger, more confident, and more zestful.

Keep Your Eyes Young

Your eyes are the best indicators of your age. If they are serene, bright, zestful, they tell the world that a young person is looking through; if they are tired, tense, lusterless, they advertise that an old person is behind them.

For years, eye doctors used the term "presbyopia" to diagnose failing eyesight in old folks, when no other definite pathological condition could be found. The term, presbyopia, means literally "old age sight." But some twenty years ago, an eminent eye doctor and surgeon, Dr. William H. Bates, startled the medical world by announcing that there was no such thing as old age sight. Poor eyesight was caused, he said, in either the young or the old, by strain and tension. Dr. Bates believed that relaxation was the secret of perfect sight, and that the more you try to see, the worse you see. Dr. Bates said that if you can learn to look without strain, without mental anxiety about seeing, if you can stop trying to make your eyes see, and relax and let them see, most of your eye troubles will cure themselves, and your eyesight will remain good well into and past what we call old age. Dr. Bates proved his theory by personally teaching hundreds of people to see better. One who benefited greatly from the Bates theory was the famous author, Aldous Huxley, who was reading braille when he met Margaret Corbett, and later learned to read a newspaper without glasses. Margaret Corbett, Dr. Bates' principal disciple, taught thousands of soldiers to see better during the last war, at her remarkable sight school in Los Angeles.

Contrary to popular belief, Dr. Bates' system did not include exercises to develop eye muscles. His whole technique was aimed at relaxing the eyes and taking the strain off the seeing mind behind them. Two of the techniques he used to achieve this were the swing, and the mental visualization of black objects. Both of these techniques are described in detail in the chapter "Mental Imagery," page 51 of this book.* Even if your sight is perfect, you will find that daily practice of these techniques will give your eyes a bright, young look, and prove to be the best beauty treatment ever devised for the eyes.

Strengthening Your Will to Live

Above all else, it is the will to live that keeps people young. The will to live, like the will to work, and the will to win, is freed by relaxation. If doubts, fears, and tension are pulling you in the opposite direction, you cannot really have the will to live.

The will is a very real force and a very powerful one. But it is not what most people suppose it to be. Will

* For readers who are interested in learning more about the way relaxation can be specifically applied to improvement of eyesight, I recommend Margaret Corbett's book, *Help Yourself to Better Sight,* Prentice-Hall, Inc., New York.

is creative and is itself subconscious. When we truly will to do something, all the forces of our minds and bodies are unified and directed toward achieving that goal. The will is not an isolated faculty that stands apart from the rest of our personality and lashes and coerces it into action.

When General Eisenhower went to Europe to try to develop the will to fight, and the will to defend themselves, among Europeans, he did not exhort them to use will power, to grit their teeth and make themselves fight whether or not they wanted to. He simply encouraged them to want to fight to defend themselves. The man with the will to fight does not have to drive himself to fight by conscious effort; the man with a will to live does not fight a part of his own personality. When we use conscious effort to exercise what we ordinarily call will power, we are not employing our true will at all. In all such circumstances we feel that we are forcing ourselves, somewhat unwillingly, or against our will, to do the thing. If we were using true will, we would be perfectly willing to do it, and no force would be necessary.

Passive relaxation, practiced every day, helps us to clear away surface conflicts and free our true will for use. Rhythmic relaxation, or relaxed doing, teaches us to function with our whole being integrated towards the task at hand, and with no contrary tensions pulling us back, or putting the brakes on our effort.

One of the greatest enemies of the will to work, the

will to win, or the will to live, is a sense of futility. If you feel deep within your heart that a certain action will prove absolutely futile, that a situation is hopeless, that failure and defeat are inevitable, you can grit your teeth all you please, but you have rendered your will powerless. We must entertain the idea of possible success before we can take the first step towards constructive action.

At the 1951 International Gerontological Congress at St. Louis, Dr. Raphael Ginzberg of Cherokee, Iowa, stated that the traditional idea, that a person is supposed to grow old and useless around seventy, is responsible in large measure for his growing old at that age. In a more enlightened future, Dr. Ginzberg said, we may come to regard seventy as middle age. The best medicine for old age, according to Dr. Ginzberg, is to give the old folks useful occupations in which their feelings of hopelessness, resignation, and futility would be banished. The man who says, "What's the use? I'm an old man," is delivering a knock-out blow to his will to live through his feeling of futility.

The widely accepted belief that once you have reached a certain age there cannot possibly be any satisfaction in store for you in the future, is one of the most common causes of a sense of futility. It may be true that you are not as young as you were once. It may be true that you cannot get satisfaction from the same things you got it from when you were twenty. But that is no reason to look forward with dread to old age. After all, at the age of twenty, you did not get satisfaction from the same things you got it from at the age of six. But you didn't sit in the corner and mope because you no longer found pleasure in toy trains and dolls. You found new satisfactions, new pleasures to fit your increased development and maturity. If the person past sixty will adopt the same attitude, he will find new interests, new enjoyments that he has grown up to and could not have enjoyed as a person of twenty or thirty. But he must have the gumption to go out and find them.

The word "incurable" is another thing that creates a sense of futility.

The November, 1951 issue of *Readers' Digest* had an article called "The Man Who Licked Cancer," by A. E. Hotchner. Mr. Hotchner tells how Lieutenant-Commander Edwin Miller Rosenberg licked an "incurable" case of cancer not once, but four times. About five years before the article appeared, a Naval doctor had told Rosenberg he had an incurable cancer, and suggested that he call in a lawyer to draw up his will. Rosenberg was given from two to three weeks to live. He was even wheeled in and exhibited to a lecture class as an incurable case.

"By the time I got back to my room, I was boiling mad," Rosenberg says. "I sent for the doctor. 'Listen,' I said, 'all day people have been saying, "Poor Rosenberg, no hope for him." The way I see it, it isn't up to the doctors to give me hope. You just do your best for me, and let me do the hoping.' "

Often, when a person has been told he has an incurable disease, he doesn't even bother to have medical treatment. Rosenberg insisted that medical treatment be begun immediately. He was determined that he had to get well so he could get back into the Navy—which was where his heart was. Radiation treatments were begun. Rosenberg got well. Then they found another cancer. In all, they found four. But Rosenberg licked them all with the help of the best medical science had to offer, and a determined will to get well and get back aboard ship—which is where he is today.

The American Cancer Society has found that fear of the word "cancer" kills almost as many—perhaps more—people as the disease itself. Believing it to be incurable, the patient does not go to his doctor in time, and, worse still, gives up the fight within himself. Rosenberg didn't depend only on the will to live. He insisted upon getting the best medical treatment he could get. But the important thing is that he did not negate the medical treatment by a feeling of futility. Working with medical science, instead of against it, he won out.

Hundreds of other people are incapacitated and even killed by another phrase, "old age." The man of thirty-five who has aches, pains, and other disease symptoms, goes to see his doctor to find out what's wrong. Too often the man of seventy diagnoses his own trouble as old age. Why bother to go to a doctor? He is an old man; the doctor can't cure that. But medical science now believes that pathological symptoms are caused by disease and malfunctioning, rather than by time, and that they are found in the young or the old.

Chapter Fifteen

The Relaxed Attitude

"Thy lot or portion of life," said the Caliph Ali, "is seeking after thee; therefore be at rest from seeking after it."

Relaxation is a way of life.

Life need not be as hectic nor as complicated and problem filled as most of us make it. A hundred years ago the words "worry" and "thought" were synonymous in the English language.

Our lives would order themselves much more wisely and efficiently if we would give up our arrogance and preoccupation with our forebrain thinking and let the mind and body work for us. Our hearts beat and our blood circulates without effort or thought on our part. Our brains would work just as effortlessly if we would let them. We need to get over the idea that we are called upon to do all our "living" by the power of our thinking forebrain, and realize that fully ninety per cent of the business of living is unconscious and automatic and beyond our direct, conscious volition.

Aldous Huxley in *The Art of Seeing* tells us that most of our troubles arise by reason of the interference of our "conscious I" into processes that it would do better to leave alone.

When John Gunther asked Vincent Sheean to tell him just how he went about the business of writing, Sheean replied: "Writing is not something that I do, it is something that is done to me. When I am writing well, it is almost as if I were taking dictation. . . . The material is poured through you."

Nearly all good writers have testified to the same sort of thing. Emerson, for example, wrote that he did not originate his thoughts by himself but that they *came* to him. He also said, "A little consideration of what takes place around us every day would show us that a higher law than our own will regulates events; that our painful labors are unnecessary, and fruitless; that only in our easy, simple, spontaneous action are we strong."

In order to have a relaxed attitude about life a man must somehow arrive at a philosophy which assures him that the heart of the universe is friendly toward him, that there is some order and plan beneath the surface of things upon which he can trust—in short, that he does not have to stay continually on the defensive against life.

Strangely enough my own faith in God was strengthened by the study of anatomy—which is supposed to have convinced others that man is a physical machine and nothing else.

The more I studied the workings of the human body, the more impressed I became with the fact that there is a system, a plan, in short an intelligence working in us for our own good. An order that not only works without our taking any thought in the matter, but of which we are for the most part totally unaware. If you cut your finger you do not have to order the cells to form scar tissue nor the blood to clot. After exertion you do not have to worry about directing your heart to beat faster. You do not have to worry about testing your blood every day to determine if the salt level has dropped below normal. If it has, you will crave more salt and restore it. These are but a few of the more obvious workings of the human body which are carried on for us without effort, volition or thought on our part. The deeper one digs into the study of anatomy, the more of these complicated mechanisms and balances one discovers, and the more one becomes convinced how very hopeless the task of maintaining and operating the human machine would be, if one were called upon to do it entirely by the power of his own conscious intellect.

A remark made by an old Negro masseur, to a tense businessman who couldn't relax, jelled my observations about the human body into a philosophy of life.

"Boss," he said, "you are worrying your brain about things that's none of your business. The Good Book says that the birds of the air and the lilies of the field get along all right and they don't think nor worry. Whatever they need is provided for them, they don't have to struggle for it nor even work for it. We're different from birds and flowers. We got a brain and we're supposed to use it. But we don't have to use it to worry about things being there. The good Lord has provided all we need to get along and he give us a brain to help us find it."

While sophisticates may smile at such a simple philosophy, it makes sense to me. Isn't the squirrel, who gathers nuts in the fall and stores them against the winter, not because of any forebrain, foresight or planning on the part of the squirrel, but just because a squirrel is built that way—because he is following an inner guidance which he neither reasons nor understands—isn't this squirrel following the same pattern I had observed in the human body? The bird that builds a nest, not because he has taken a course in nest-engineering, nor because his superior intellect has decided that a nest is necessary, but because it is provided in the nature of things for birds to build nests, isn't the bird following the same pattern?

Aren't the squirrel, the bird, the lily of the field showing evidence that they are in essence organs in a larger body of things; guided and provided for much as the organs in the human body are directed by a power not of man's intellect?

Doesn't this indicate that the squirrel, the bird and the lily are not standing alone in the universe, but are part of something bigger than themselves?

And if this is true of the squirrel, the bird and the lily, would not the same be true of man, and in a much larger, grander sense?

The forebrain, or the thinking part of our brain, is an important part of our mental machinery, but it is, after all, just a part. I like to think of it as comparable to an engineer on a train. The engineer must use judgment, give orders, make decisions. He does not furnish the driving power that turns the wheels. He is not responsible for laying out the tracks ahead of him. He does not have to worry about the very existence of his destination.

It is a sad commentary on our modern civilization that we have so abused and misused our forebrains that "prefrontal lobotomy" has become a commonplace phrase in our language. This operation literally handcuffs the engineer so that he can do no more mischief. It obliterates worry, depression and neurotic fear by severing the nerves to the midbrain. But it also obliterates caution, judgment and creative imagination.

I do not mean to imply that thinking in itself is an evil. It is man's distinguishing and most prized ability. Man needs to think, and to think clearly, today, perhaps, as never before in history. But we cannot use our forebrain to do the job it was meant to do—to think and reason—if we load it down with jobs and responsibilities it was never meant to have. We cannot think clearly if our minds are muddled with fears, anxieties and tensions.

Nor do I believe that a man should sit and hold his hands when there is work to be done, with the consolation that he will be taken care of. What my own relaxed attitude has done has been to relieve me of a vast load of care and responsibilities about outcomes and results. It has taught me that if a man will relax and do his work, he can well relieve himself of concern about the results of his work; that if a man will do the best he can and the best he knows, he has done all he was ever supposed to do.

Insecurity and Tension

A seriously neurotic person cannot learn to swim. He cannot trust himself to the water to hold him up. He will not allow himself to sink down into the water deeply enough so that the water can support him. If you take a deep breath and jump feet first into a pool of water and do nothing whatsoever, your body will rise to the top so that the very top of your head will be above water. It then takes but the slightest downward push with your hands to raise yourself the few inches necessary to get your mouth above the water line so that you can breathe.

If you are afraid to allow yourself to sink down into the water deeply enough so that the water can support you, and begin to fight wildly to keep your whole upper body out of the water, you will sink.

My friend, Fred R. Lanoue, swimming instructor at Georgia Tech., has taught many people how to stay afloat, with water over their heads for as long as ten hours at a time. Many of these people couldn't even swim. The secret of his method is to have the pupil take a deep breath, jump in feet first, and make no attempt to keep his head above water. He *relaxes completely* with his face just under the water line, and *lets the water hold him up*. He holds his breath for twenty seconds or more, then lets it out smoothly and at the same time, makes a gentle downward push with either hands or feet, just enough to get his mouth above the water line. He gulps in another lungful of air, relaxes, and allows himself to sink down once again.

Tense people all make the same mistake. They struggle desperately to keep their heads above water. Yet, if they would only let themselves sink down another couple of inches they would find that life itself would hold them up. Lanoue tells his pupils: "Don't try to float yourself. Let the water float you." He also says: "Don't fight the water, don't struggle, don't try too hard. Remember, only a gentle push every now and then is all you need."

There are two significant characteristics of our present civilization. One is the wide-spread preoccupation with material security. The other is the prevalence of nervous breakdowns and ills growing out of emotional tension. It is time we realized that in pursuing material- istic security we are chasing a will-o'-the-wisp. Our real security is not in things, whether they be dollars in a bank, stocks and bonds, or our name in gold upon a door.

Our real security lies in our ability to function.

It is the ability to function that enables a man to acquire wealth, a good job, or any other material symbol of security, in the first place.

If you had a machine that turned out a hundred ten-dollar bills an hour, you would not be so foolish as to give your entire concern to guarding, counting and storing the ten-dollar bills. Instead your real concern would be to keep the machine functioning at its best. Nor would you live in continual anxiety lest one of the ten-dollar bills be taken from you. Yet that is a pretty good picture of the attitude many of us have in our preoccupation with material security, a quest that burns out our machines, gives us nervous breakdowns, freezes our brains so that we cannot think clearly.

Preoccupation with, and undue concern over, material security causes tension. Tension, in turn, incapacitates both our mental and physical mechanisms, keeps them from functioning at their best.

Getting Something for Nothing

The twin brother of the abnormal desire for material security is the hope of getting something for nothing.

Many tense people face life with the defensive attitude: "I hope nothing happens to upset my plans." Their attitude is that of a man standing before a roulette wheel. There is no known law or order that he can depend upon. He is at the mercy of luck. The uncertainty and lack of inner security that such a belief engenders is bound to make one tense. You cannot relax if you feel the ground is liable to open and swallow you at any moment.

Give up your desire to get something for nothing, and you give up at the same time your fear and anxiety that you won't. You then free your energies for creative accomplishment. If we are concerned with dealing with problems rather than escaping from them, they can become a source of exhilaration.

Learn to "Give" a Little

Many tense, rigid people unconsciously carry with them a stiff unbending attitude toward life. This type of tense person is even sometimes described as "stiff-necked." He is uncompromising and prides himself upon what he likes to call his principles, but which are more likely to be his unbending prejudices. He tends to be intolerant of others. Life can be pretty rugged with such stiff, tense, unbending attitudes.

One of the first things I try to teach boys in gym boxing classes is to roll with the punch. Rolling with the punch doesn't mean that you are letting the punch overcome you, as many uncompromising people who won't give an inch seem to think. When you roll with a punch you do not try to stop the blow with your chin. You go with it a little way, rob it of its power to hurt you, and recover yourself.

Learn to give in a little to the hard knocks of life and they won't hurt you nearly so much. An automobile which has no springs and cannot give to the bumps in the road would soon be shaken to pieces. Trees that do not bend with the wind are broken. If you are sitting where you can look out over the wings of a large airliner while the ship is in rough weather, you can see the huge wings bending up and down over an arc of several feet. This is not because the wings are weak or because the winds are getting the best of the wings. The wings are built that way to absorb shocks.

Relaxation, relaxed living and relaxed attitudes are valuable shock absorbers that enable us to ride out rough spots in life without being broken by them.

Summary

Here, then, are the ways to use relaxation to stay well and to feel alive as long as you live:

1. Practice passive relaxation every day to tone down your nervous system, and to reduce your over-response and over-defense against stress situations.

2. Learn rhythmic relaxation so that you can work and play without tension and conflict.

3. Develop a relaxed philosophy of life—a way of looking at things that will enable you to take difficult situations in your stride.

4. Slow down. Take your time. Don't hurry through life. Your whole being is geared to function in one small area at a time, on one thing at a time. The only way you can live without strain is to do your living now —in the present moment.

5. Fear, doubt, and a sense of futility, cause tension, and defeat your will. Give up fighting negatives and direct your energies toward accomplishing the positive.

Always act as if success and the satisfactory outcome were inevitable.

6. Don't let the words incurable and old age keep you from seeking medical treatment if you are not well. Don't try to use relaxation to cure anything except tension. See your doctor regularly for periodic check-ups. This in itself will enable you to relax to an extraordinary degree. Many people go on for years, tensed up by the vague fear that there may be something wrong with them, and yet are afraid to see their doctor. Transfer this responsibility to your doctor, and you can relax. Fear of the unknown makes you tense. The truth, even when it is bad, allows you to relax and accept a situation, and begin to deal with it. Doubts and uncertainties keep you in continual tension. Only your doctor can settle your doubts about your health.

Perhaps, for many years, you have been beset by fears and anxieties that have made you tense. You have felt that you must concern yourself with these negatives, that you must fear failure, that you must constantly stay on guard against the things you don't want to happen. Perhaps you have used up so much energy staying on the defensive that you have little energy left for an offensive of your own. Perhaps you have sensed that such a waste of energy is slowly killing you, and taking all the joy out of living. If so, why not throw all the fears and anxieties overboard, and *Relax And Live*!